Sex Positions for Couples

2 Books in 1: The Ultimate Guide with Sexual Positions, Tantric Massage, Kama Sutra and Sexy Games for Adults. Now You Discover How to Talk Dirty and HAVE BETTER SEX.

by Monika Bielska

Sommario

SEX FOR COUPLES

Introduction

What is Intimacy?

There are different types of intimacy, and I will outline them for you before digging deeper into the intimacy that exists between couples. Intimacy, in a general sense, is defined as mutual openness and vulnerability between two people. There are different ways in which you can give and receive openness and vulnerability in a relationship. Intimacy does not have to include a sexual relationship (though it can); therefore, it is not solely reserved for romantic relationships. Intimacy can also be present in other types of close relationships like friendships or family relationships. Below, I will outline the different forms of intimacy.

Emotional Intimacy

Emotional intimacy is the ability to express oneself in a mature and open manner, leading to a deep emotional connection between people. Saying things like "I love you" or "you are very important to me" are examples of this. It is also the ability to respond in a mature and open way when someone expresses themselves to you by saying things like "I'm sorry" or "I love you too." This type of open and vulnerable dialogue leads to an emotional connection. In order for a deep emotional connection to form, there must be a mutual willingness to be vulnerable and open with one's deeper thoughts and feelings. This is where this type of emotional intimacy comes from.

Intellectual Intimacy

Intellectual intimacy is a kind of intimacy that involves discussing and sharing thoughts and opinions on intellectual matters, from which they gain fulfillment and feelings of closeness with the other person. For example, if you are discussing politics with someone who you deem to be an intellectual equal you may find that you feel a closeness with them as you share your thoughts and opinions and connect on an intellectual level. Many people find intellect and brains to be sexy in a partner!

Shared Interests and Activities as a Form of Intimacy

This form of intimacy is less well-known, but it is also considered a form of intimacy. When you share activities with another person that you both enjoy and are passionate about, this creates a sense of connection. For example, when you cook together or travel together. These shared experiences give you memories to share and this leads to bonding and intimacy (openness and vulnerability). This type of connection is usually present in friendships, in familial relationships and, more importantly, in romantic relationships. Being able to share interests and activities leads to a closeness that can be defined as intimacy.

Physical Intimacy

Physical intimacy is the type that most people think of when they hear the term "intimacy". It also involves other non-sexual types of physical contact such as hugging and kissing. Physical intimacy can be found in close friendships or familial relationships where hugging and kisses on the cheek are common, but it is most often found in romantic relationships.

Physical intimacy is the type of intimacy involved when people are trying to make each other orgasm. Physical intimacy is almost always required for orgasm. Physical intimacy doesn't necessarily mean that you are in love with the person you are having sex with; it just means that you are doing something intimate with another person in a physical way.

It is also possible to be intimate with yourself, and while this begins with the emotional intimacy of self-awareness, it also involves the physical intimacy of masturbation and physical self-exploration. I define sexual, the physical intimacy of the self as being in touch with the parts of yourself physically that you would not normally be in touch with. If you are a woman, these parts include your breasts, your clitoris, your vagina, and your anus. If you are a man, these parts include your testicles, your penis, and your anus. Being able to be physically intimate with yourself allows you to have more fulfilling sex, more fulfilling orgasms and a more fulfilling overall relationship with your body. Allowing someone to be physically intimate with you in a sexual way is also an emotionally intimate experience, regardless of your relationship with the person. Being in charge of your own body while it is in the hands of another person is very important and this is why masturbation is such a key element to physical intimacy.

You can think of physical intimacy as something that breaks the barrier of personal space. By this definition, this includes touching of any sort, but especially sexual intercourse, kissing touching and anything else of a sexual nature. When you are having sex with anyone, regardless of whether you have romantic feelings for them or not, you are having a physically intimate relationship with them. The difference between a relationship that involves physical intimacy alone and no other forms of intimacy and a romantic relationship is that a romantic relationship will also involve emotional intimacy, shared activities and intellectual intimacy is that a deep and lasting romantic relationship will need to include all of these forms of intimacy at once.

How to Increase Intimacy

For a romantic relationship to be successful, there must be several forms of intimacy shared between the partners. Without a combination of all of the forms of intimacy, there is nothing that sets a romantic relationship apart from an everyday friendship.

It is important to communicate about your needs for intimacy with your partner so that they know what is important to you and what you need from them for the relationship to be successful. Further, this must be tackled on a recurring basis since people will grow and change over the course of their relationship and both partners must be aware of the changes in the needs of their romantic partner. This is especially important in a long-term relationship, as being aware of when a person's intimacy needs change is important to maintaining a good level of intimacy and a deep connection.

Communication

Communication is the key in a relationship of any sort, but especially in a romantic relationship. Communicating is the only sure way to know where the other person stands in terms of their thoughts, feelings and needs. Being able to be vulnerable and open with your emotions is a requirement for any type of intimacy, and this involves being vulnerable and open about your needs for intimacy itself. It is necessary to share oneself with the other person in a relationship. This mutual sharing of yourselves is what will lead to intimacy in the first place as well as an increase in your level of intimacy.

Sometimes in a long-term relationship, you become so comfortable with each other that you begin to feel like you don't have to communicate with your partner as much as you once did. You may begin to feel like they can read your thoughts and your feelings, since you know each other so well. While this is a great point to reach in a relationship, this can sometimes lead to a breakdown in communication. It is important to maintain communication in order to avoid miscommunications or misunderstandings that can happen when both parties think that the other person can read their mind. The key here is to continue communicating, even if you think the other person knows what you are thinking or feeling without you having to say it. By doing this, you keep the lines of communication open in your relationship at all times. It is better to over-communicate than to under-communicate in a romantic relationship. This avoids any chance of miscommunication or misunderstanding that would be perpetuated by a lack of communication. By having misunderstandings go unresolved, this could lead to resentment and an overall breakdown in communication, which can reduce levels of intimacy in the relationship.

Orgasm

The orgasm is the culmination of a sexual relationship, a climax that produces a pleasant feeling of a sudden release of accumulated tension from the moment when the excitement phase begins. It is at that moment that a series of intense muscle spasms are generated that are highly pleasing, which helps the release of endorphins that occurs simultaneously.

Women experience orgasm in different ways, but usually, this is characterized by the fact that the acceleration of heart rate, breathing, and blood pressure reach their highest level and the vagina, uterus, anus, and muscles Pelvic bones contract between five and ten times at intervals of less than one second. However, some women may feel orgasm throughout their body and even multiple orgasms.

In the case of men, we must bear in mind that ejaculation and orgasm are not the same. You can ejaculate without experiencing orgasm. As in women, with orgasm, heart rate, breathing, and blood pressure are accelerated to the maximum, and muscle contractions occur in the pelvic area, as well as the prostate and seminal vesicles to produce the expulsion of the semen.

The orgasm lasts only a few moments and then enters what is known as the resolution phase in which there is a general relaxation of the whole body, normalization of blood circulation and breathing, and with it a feeling of great placidity, tiredness, and even drowsiness.

The lack of control over ejaculation, as in the case of premature ejaculation, can make a man unable to reach orgasm. Similarly, many women confess not to reach it regularly and even never (anorgasmia). It is very important that the couple talks about it because experimentation and information can improve their sexual practice and learn to control ejaculation in the case of men and enhance their excitement in the woman. Couples therapy can be a good option to solve this sexual dysfunction.

How Are Male And Female Orgasms Different?

The female orgasm

Contractions start at 0.8-second intervals and their number can vary greatly, decreasing after intensity, duration, and frequency. More than a localized response in the pelvis, it is a total response of the organism. Imagination is directly related to orgasm, the brain has a lot to do with it. With the penetration, the entire vulvar pyramid is mobilized synchronously and the G-spot and the clitoris are stimulated. Every woman has the physical ability to experience orgasms.

These are the symptoms of female orgasm :

• 	Greater increase in heart rate.

• 	Increase in breathing

• 	Increase in blood pressure.

• 	The subjective sensation of the explosion of pleasure.

• 	Contraction of the uterus.

Contraction of the orgasmic platform.

After the orgasm, there would be a recovery in the woman prior to the excitement. Although if it is restimulated before the sexual tension decreases, the woman is able to present several successive orgasms.

The Female Orgasm: Keys To Reach It

The female orgasm is not only achieved through penetration. It is highly recommended to explore the female body to discover erogenous zones that facilitate the task. In the case of sexual intercourse, preliminaries, oral sex, and other pleasurable practices can be the perfect vehicle to achieve an unforgettable orgasm. Meanwhile, it is also essential:

•   That your partner knows how to "work" better to "play" and experience things with you

to know oneself through self-exploration. So, if you want to enjoy your body and your areas of pleasure, try one of these useful toys.

1.   Physical manifestations of female orgasm

During orgasm:

•   the clitoris retracts,

•   the vagina, the perineum and the uterus contract due to shaking

•   the nipples harden

•   the heart accelerates

the blood vessels dilate.

Everything is stimulated during this supreme pleasure with which women (and men, in their case) go mad. And it is normal because the orgasm involves secretion of endorphins, the molecule of happiness, which provides a feeling of unequaled well-being.

2.   How to achieve a female orgasm

In general, most women achieve orgasm when they stimulate sexual areas alone or in pairs:

•   Preliminary caresses: activate your brain preparing for the moment of intercourse. These movements increase the pleasure much more and reach orgasm before.

•   cunnilingus: is one of the techniques that most excites women and that will favor that if you have anorgasmia you can get to reach orgasm.

- masturbation: whether you do it yourself or your partner will get the genital area excited more easily.

penetration: through the penis the woman also reach orgasm. It is one of the most essential parts that lead us to intercourse, to the female orgasm, and also to the ejaculation of man.

But the best way to reach orgasm is knowing the body of one. We have different erogenous points that are able to make us feel in the seventh heaven, but you have to find them!

The solution: start in the discovery of the body:

- alone or as a couple,

- with sexual toys

without them, to detect the most moving areas.

3.   Different female orgasms

Vaginal orgasm: is achieved by stimulation of the Gräfenberg point or more commonly called "G-spot", located about 4 cm from the entrance of the vagina. It has a ball shape of less than one centimeter and increases in size with stimulation. It is located next to the bladder so it is not strange that after a vaginal female orgasm we feel like going to the bathroom. To sensitize, stimulate it regularly with gentle and repeated pressures with the point of the finger or with the help of a sex toy. Try these toys if you want to get an incredible vaginal orgasm:

- Massager vibrator with 30 different modes.

- Chinese vibrating silicone balls with remote control.

Vibrator with heat effect for women.

Clitoral orgasm : is achieved by stimulation of the clitoris. That is a small button located between the lips, anterior to the vagina. It is accessed very easily. It is very sensitive. You can reach orgasm with delicate caresses. Here we leave you a few positions that will facilitate the pleasant task. These are the best sex toys to stimulate the clitoris:

- Satisfier Pro, clitoral sniffer.

- Clitoral massager with cunnilingus effect.

Vibrator clitoris massager.

4.   The female orgasm, in figures

Clitorian orgasm: according to a study 95% of women come to him through masturbation and less than half, 45% share it with the male penis.

The vaginal orgasm: there are few women who manage to reach this orgasm. Only 30% have the pleasure of experiencing such pleasure. Although we all have a G-spot, we have to get "wake up" with multiple movements in this area. For this, there are positions that favor it: the missionary, with the legs of the woman on the back of the man or the greyhound, with which a deep penetration is facilitated.

5.   Female multiorgasm is possible

Although for some it is only a fantasy, the truth is that multiorgasm exists and is easier to achieve than it seems. The key is in:

- know your own body,

- know what is possible

- put our mind on it,

- lengthen the sexual climax (many times we do not achieve it because our partner lasts less than we would like),

- go changing stimuli and erogenous zones

choose postures that really work with us

The Male Orgasm

There are between 3 and 10 contractions with an interval of 8 tenths of a second between each one, depending on how intense the response is. This means that an orgasm lasts on average between 4 and 8 seconds. Man experiences this physiological reaction as a wave of pleasurable sensations.

These are the symptoms of male orgasm :

- Greater increase in heart rate.

- Increase in breathing

- Increase in blood pressure.

- The subjective sensation of the explosion of pleasure.

- Contraction of the penis, urethra, and sphincter.

Expulsion of semen abroad.

After the orgasm, in man, there would be the recovery of the state prior to the excitement and the refractory period would begin, by which the man will not be aroused again after some time, something that can vary according to each person.

The Male Orgasm: Keys to Reach It

Orgasms during sex are better than during masturbation.

Ejaculating usually reduces the risk of cancer

Men who ejaculated more frequently (about 21 times a month) reduced their risk of prostate cancer by 20 %. This benefit is since during the orgasm, different hormones are released, such as oxytocin (known as lowering blood pressure, for example).

The male and female orgasms are more similar than it seems

Despite the difference in orgasm between men and women, there is no variation between the duration and intensity of orgasm concerning sex. What does offer opposition is that the orgasms are different in each person and can be divided into two main types: the usual orgasm, the most common, consisting of about 6-15 high-intensity contractions for about 20-30 seconds or orgasm prolonged, in which regular contractions are experienced after the initial orgasm, which can last between 30 and 90 seconds.

Male ejaculation is as fast as ...

The average speed of a man's ejaculation is 45 kilometers per hour. Taking into account that Usain Bolt runner holds the record of 44.72 kilometers per hour, the rate of ejaculation is faster than the fastest man on the face of the Earth.

Erotic Games

Respecting Your Partner

1.   Consent: The first way to ensure that erotic games and role play are a fun and safe experience for all that are involved is to ensure that everyone is on board with what is happening. This means that you ask for your partner before you start these games what is and isn't acceptable for them. Some partners will not like anal sex and it is important to respect those boundaries even in a game where one person is in the controlling or dominant role.

2.   Safety: Protecting yourself and your partner from sexually transmitted infections is an important step to take. If you have not been tested in a long time, it is important to make an appointment at a local clinic or your private doctor to make sure that you are free from any sexually transmitted diseases. If you are not, it is important to discuss those risks with your partner, as they should have consent in whether or not they have sexual interaction with someone who has a STI or STD. Should you not want to get tested, or have sex with multiple partners, it is important to wear protection.

3.   Birth Control: If you are not planning on having children with your partner, it is important to discuss the ramifications of the sex act and what you plan to do to protect against having children. There are many forms of birth control available from the temporary like condoms to more longer lasting options. Longer lasting options include birth control pills, rings and patches, and IUD's and implants. Each method has their own benefits and detriments so it is important to talk with your gynecologist about them. For men there aren't nearly as many options but you can talk with your physician to see what options are currently available including the more permanent options like vasectomies.

4.   Clarity: While this falls under consent it is important to ensure that you do not engage in sexual intercourse with someone that is clearly overly inebriated on alcohol or other substances. This is important because it shows respect for your partner by saying that you care about their mental well-being and understand that under the state of diminished mental capacity, they do not have the ability to make sound decisions about their sexuality.

5.   Relaxing: It is important to show respect to your partner by creating a relaxing atmosphere to have sexual activity that is relaxing for your partner, this does not exclude BDSM related dungeons and other facilities as those can be relaxing to depending upon your fetishes. A relaxing atmosphere is one that is free from judgement and ridicule of their body and fantasies as well as one that respects their safety and privacy concerns.

Erotic Games

Having taken the steps to ensure a respectful tone of events you are ready to begin your journey into increased eroticism. While these games aren't necessarily Tantra, they help to relax the mind and body and allow you to experience new sides of your partners sexuality. Here is a list of erotic games that you can try with your partner to decrease your inhibitions and allow yourselves to connect at a deeper level sexually. Try and choose three of these games that you want to try.

•   Make an appointment in a hotel bar or restaurant, as if you didn't know each other, then take a room in the hotel and love each other as if it were the first night.

•   Enjoy a candlelight dinner: the male partner brings a bouquet of fragrant flowers whose color reflects something he particularly appreciates in her, and she wears the dress that makes her feel most desirable.

•   Make love with your partner while someone else is watching.

•   Blindfold your partner and tie him and play with respect to his limits but in a BDSM context

•   Have sex outside, with respect to the laws of your location.

•   Try group sex

•   Go hiking and make love on the top of a mountain

•   Imitate animals having sex, choose exotic animals and have fun imagining ways that they might have sex.

•   Try six different positions while trying to keep the insertion in place.

•   Try anal sex.

- Caress your partner with scarves, feathers, and a silk cloth.

- Spread honey on the neck, on the breast, on the stomach, on the thighs and lick it off your partner.

- Try some consensual non-consent play where you pretend as if you are reluctant in the sexual act.

- Play doctor.

- Play naked twister

- Oil each other up and slide your oily naked bodies on top of each other while having sex

- Try your own fantasy

You may have thought of other ideas that are more exciting to you while listening to this list. It is also possible that none of these ideas seemed to your taste, try something different and see how well you can turn your partner on. Whatever you have decided after you have three ideas of what to try with your partner, get together and do the following:

1.   Tell each other which of the erotic games you would like to try.

2.   Invite your partner to try them with you.

3.   Allow your partner to propose variations to make them more comfortable.

4.   After you try each game exchange thoughts about the experience with each other.

This game should have helped you to discover your hidden fantasies. Your hidden fantasies are precious and allow us to make new discoveries about ourselves. These fantasies show us the way to new discoveries, they tell us where we can find the stimuli that make our reality more intense, where we can seek, discover and grow. In Tantra they say, "everything is allowed, there are no taboos, everything can be tried" meaning that everything that stimulates us and makes us feel good, will help to makes us feel more complete.

Beware, if you do these erotic games or other games of your choosing mechanically and without awareness or without grasping the energy that is released in the moment you will lose out on a valuable experience. This is a spiritual journey, like Tantra, remember to respect your partner and to discover new things about yourself. It is why the discussion about respect was so important because these games are to help us discover more about our partners, not just get off. These erotic games are to help you to challenge yourself and discover more about your partner, this is why Tantra is also called "the way of pleasure".

Along this route, it is good to always have some principles in mind:

1.   The fear is usually equal to the desire. If you have a fear of performing you have a desire to perform.

2.   The greater the fear, the stronger the desire.

3.   Following our desires, gives us an energy charge.

4.   For every wish fulfilled, we will discover others.

5.   The way of desires is not always linear. We may discover yearnings for the opposite of our desires as we fulfill a desire

The boundary between the known and the unknown, between habitual and new, is not a clear and distinct furrow, but a band of reality marked by two openings in front of us, that is, by two lines that invite us to go beyond them. Once we cross one threshold, we may find everything stimulating and while we may have fears, we will also have curiosity. We can always decide to go further or to withdraw from the game. If we go further and meet the second opening, fear may become overwhelming, but take time to decide to go further as you may regret it. But remember if you risk nothing, you gain no knowledge of yourself.

There is an art to exploring. The art consists in remaining between the two thresholds, in not falling back into the boredom of the known or into the abyss of dangerous lands, remaining in that intermediate belt where we feel intrigued and at the same time safe. This is how you discover new landscapes of yourself and dare to discover others.

Remember that we each have two souls in ourselves; one that pushes and the other brakes. If after some erotic game we note that the band between the two thresholds seem very narrow, it means that in us the shy part and the courageous part are in conflict.

Exorcising Inhibitions Exercise

To start a negotiation between these two parts of yourself there is an exercise you can try. The exorcising inhibitions exercise allows you to imagine your shy side and your brave side as two distinct characters. Here is how to do this exercise.

1.   Imagine two characters each a few feet apart and a few feet in front of you. Imagine them well, give them details and characteristics. Maybe the brave side is played by a fierce knight with a big sword and the shy side is played by a humble stable boy. Whatever you imagine, imagine it in detail. Give them voices and gestures, in your mind.

2.   Observe the characteristics of both of these characters.

3.   Ask yourself in which instances are these characters correct about their assumptions of things.

4.   If at the beginning you are more attracted to on character over the other ask yourself why and think of the possible negative consequences of always listening to the one character. Maybe we would become bank robbers if we always acted out of daring, or maybe we would have never taken a chance to ask out our partner if we never took a chance like the shy character would have liked. Imagine what it would be like if they were each alone, without the other to temper them.

5.   Ask yourself what they gain if they are together and how they support each other.

6.   Imagine yourself as the shy side moving slowly to the place where the brave hero stood. Imagine him shedding the skin of the shy stable boy to become the courageous knight bringing with him all the good qualities that come with being timid and taking on all the good qualities of being brave.

7.   Begin to feel like the new character, the new character is a person that is no longer in conflict with the two parts of their personality but knows how to navigate the world with both their timid and brave sides in harmony.

By trying this exercise, you will find that you are able to understand why you must remain between the two thresholds of your personality. That by following the direction of the two parts of you that you find balance. The more you manage to integrate the two parts of yourself the less inner conflict you will have. You will begin to move in the high energy area that is the world between the two thresholds. This does not just apply to erotic games but to all the challenges and changes that we encounter on life's journey.

Essential information from the Kamasutra

One of the best-known works of the east is the Kamasutra of Vatsyayana. Other well-known books are that of the Kokasastra of Kokkoka, the Tibetan Kamasastra and the Chinese Fangchungshu. These are all books that intend to enlarge the map of eroticism, find new ways of uniting, and help people get out of their habits. There is; however, danger in taking them as simple techniques as if they are sex gymnastics. These are positions that are intended to induce certain moods and atmosphere to create a sense of togetherness.

Some care must be taken with experimenting with new positions. The six most important factors to consider to ensure quality energy charge and a high degree of awareness when making love are the following:

1.   Breath: We must first evaluate if you can breathe freely in a particular position, if this is not taken care of not only will we not be able to charge our energy we can run the risk of suffocation.

2.   Pelvic Movement: Ensure that you can manage to rotate it and move it freely

3.   Hands: Make sure that your hands are free to touch and caress your partner even when you are not having penetrative sex.

4.   Position: Ensure that it is a relaxing position to keep for a prolonged period, again evaluate if you can support either your own or your partner's weight in this position.

5.   Look: Can you look into your partner's eyes and communicate to them freely with all your heart through nonverbal communication.

6.   Support: Is this a good position to have support in, can you find a more supportive position to hold.

As for positions in these books, they can easily be divided into four broadly defined categories.

1.   man above, woman below

2.   woman above, man below

3.   from behind

4.   tantric positions

Each of these positions gives a particular color to the sexual act. In the first two positions, the "above" and the "below" are often connected with controlling and submitting, given that the partner above is favored in driving the rhythm and the movement. In regards to these above and below positions it is worth trying the various types of positions that are available. Try them and see how both you and your partner feel.

Positions from behind, or "behind", usually solicit a very corporeal, animalistic, passionate sexuality. These are positions that allow you to make more love at the 1st level of the chakra, also known as pure sex with a deeper sense of penetration depending on the length of the vaginal canal and the penis. Furthermore, depending upon the angle, these positions can stimulate the g-spot more easily.

The Tantric positions usually have the partners on the same level and are very useful for tantric sexual exercises.

One such position that has an advantage in Tantric sexual relations is Scissors position. This position is suitable for making love in a relaxed way for a long time.

In this position the man is able to adjust the balance between excitement and the containment of his energy charge while slowly moving the pelvic region. He will be able to control any rapidly approaching orgasm by adjusting the rhythm and slowing it down to give him a moment to charge and release some of that sexual energy that has built inside of him. Another advantage of this position is that it allows the woman to reach her clitoris with her hand and allows her to excite herself easily. Finally, this position allows both partners to remain in good visual contact and have their hands free to caress each other during their union.

How the Scissors Position is Performed:

The male and female lie joined at the genitals both of them with their legs intertwined but their bodies aligned in opposite directions, they are head to toe and toe to head.

However, it is important to remember that in any position it is important to communicate with your partner based on the six factors above as any position can become uncomfortable depending upon your body, feelings or any thoughts that may arise during your union.

The Techniques Of Tantra Massage For Beginners

Here are some tips and tricks to learn about tantra that'll help you. These ten tips will change your life, change your mindset, and help you improve the experience too.

Stretching and Preparing

As we've said before, your breathing is very important for tantra, but you also should remember that getting the body nice and limber is really good too. When you do this, try to empty your mind of every negative thought that's there, and everything that's holding you back. This should be an experience of, as you stretch out and prepare the body, practically imagine all of the tensions going away. The more you get rid of, the lighter you'll be.

You should also, right before the experience, work through everything that's bothering your spiritual growth, and what's holding you back from enjoying tantric sex with your partner and put them down somewhere. This will help you improve your mindset and experience when doing tantra.

Mind the Temperature of Your Home

Most don't realize that the temperature of their home plays a big part in the way tantric sex goes. Yes, your home can be too cold, and that affects the overall feeling of tantric sex. What's the best way to combat this?

Well, try to keep it in a way where it's around 72 degrees at all times. It's a comfy temperature, and you can always leave the heat on about an hour or so to make it nice and cozy if it's very cold outside. If it's warm, turn on the arid conditioner, but set it around 70 degrees, so that space is nice and cool, but it isn't too chilly for you two either.

Scents Galore

One way to really bring the place to a new level and to enhance your experience is the scent. Scented candles are good, and scented candles will add a romantic touch to it. But, if you really want to make the place smell good, try diffusing an essential oil in the space, whatever essential oil you like. I like lavender a lot because it's got a calming feel to it and smells great.

But another great one is to burn incense sticks, or even just put flowers somewhere in the room to add a nice touch.

The idea behind his is to add a little touch to your space. When it comes to choosing scents, pick something you like that's pleasurable, but also not so overwhelming or irritating to your senses. So, maybe a big bowl of potpourri may be a bad idea, but a little bit of rose essential oil diffused or worn around your neck will give that alluring, sensual feeling to it.

Be Mindful

One big thing with this is you need to be mindful of both the emotions and sensations. The biggest thing to remember is that your mind will wander, and that's normal. However, when it does wander, acknowledge, and bring it back. You should also pay full attention to how the body is feeling during these experiences.

You also may experience a full range of emotions as well, and that's normal for you to do too. This is a way for you to experience everything that's happening, letting you tap into your energy and power that's there. The emotions that you experience are certainly better than what you may experience as well, and you should always make sure that, when you do this, you try to really let go and understand yourself. Sometimes, you might feel a little frustrated. Understand that it's your body and mind reacting to this, and sometimes, it takes aba bit to get used to. But, that's okay, because once you get into the moment, it can be a rewarding experience.

Cuddling

Remember that tantric sex isn't just having sex, but sometimes, laying together and cuddling is a way to nurture this. Sometimes, snuggling close together with the hearts and stomachs lined up. The giver should then have their arms around he one receiving, and their hand over the receiver's heart, and the receiver can rest their hand on top of here. One way to get you both into the mood is to just lay here and harmonize your breath and let the energy flow between you. This is a good thing to do after you've experienced intercourse because it helps to bring forth that connection with the other being that you might've not had before.

Focus on the energy you're putting forth between the two of you as this happens, and laying together along with cuddling is a wonderful way to help you experience the fun in each and every single moment, and you will, in turn, build a better, more loving experience with your partner, and it will help with aligning the energies between both of you.

Setting the Intention

The intention that you have in place and connection we put forth is very important. This is something you should have when you're starting with tantra, and through each session. No matter what, figure out your intention, whether it be to improve your sex life, or just strengthen the relationship between both of you, you've got to set the intention to practice this. Setting your intention will help keep both of you grounded, and help you get the most that you can out of this.

Sometimes, we don't set the intention of what we're doing, and that poses a problem. Most people who don't set it before going not a tantric experience will realize they're no in the right place and they're not getting what they want out of the session. The intention in tantric sex, whether it be through masturbation, massaging, penetration, or the like, always needs to be there, and you should set this up before you get anywhere with this. The intention is how you get everything in place, and how you get everything that you want out of it, so you'll definitely want to make sure the intent is set before you begin anything else. The intention should also be a big part of this, and you should also make sure you both remember when you do this.

Don't Always Be Naked

Just like how tantric sex doesn't require you to have penetration, understand that you can do this both clothed and naked. You can either do this with the clothes fully on, or you can remove every piece of fabric that you have on your body. But this is a personal thing with you.

Remember you can have sex with clothes on. That's one of the beauties of sex. You don't have to be naked, and sometimes, stimulating the senses in ways other than just sex might be wonderful for you.

The key here is whatever makes you comfortable, so if you're comfy with being naked, then by all means, you go for it. If you notice that you're better off being naked, then do that. Remember, it's your experience, and you need to figure out for yourself what type of disarray you're willing to be in.

The same goes for your partner. If you know your partner is comfier with his shirt on, then leave the shirt on. The same goes for bottoms. Looser clothing makes this part easier, so that's why it's encouraged to wear loose-fitting clothing when you do engage in tantric sex because that alone will help you with putting forth the effort to really experience and engage with one another as well.

Focus on going slow

Slow and steady wins the race, and that's something you should remember with tantric sex. The big thing to remember is that going slow is the big focal part here. Never try to rush tantra, because it dilutes the experience. What you need to do, is get into the mindset where you're relaxed and able to enjoy every moment of the practice, since that alone will help you immensely with the full benefits of tantra.

Remember, you can focus on all parts of the body, and everything that is going on. Try stroking your hands on or over your partner's body, and you should try to move slower.ly. use your tongue to explore the mouth while you kiss, and the way you move your tongue against theirs. Try gently moving your lips up and down on their chest and have them do the same.

You shouldn't rush this. The idea is to fully savor the moment, to enhance the experience like this, and to fully immerse yourself at the moment, and to experiment with this.

You Don't Have to Go Full Tantra

Sometimes you look at this and wonder if you need to start practicing this as a ritual. No way, that's not the case. Sometimes, this incorporates foreplay and meditation together, or even just focusing on your breath while pleasuring your partner. Sometimes, this means after sex you just sit around and cuddle one another and make it so that both of you are happy with one another and the way that you feel. The idea behind tantra is that you don't need to completely change up your sex life for this. There is no right or wrong way to do it, other than the basic rushing and moving too fast with tantra. The big thing to remember is that you can enjoy the moment and the experience of tantra, and work to better each and every single moment of tantra s you go along. Incorporating these elements might also be a good way to get your partner into the fun of using tantra.

Try out Experimental Positions

Tantra isn't something that you have to do by rote. It's never a rote experience, but rather, it's something that you work on, getting better over time, and work to master. The best way to do this is to try out something new.

The idea is to explore your partner. Even though it might be a place that normally isn't explored, a hint of exploring can do you some good. And who knows, your partner might like it too.

The idea behind this is, of course, similar to kink and other types of experimenting. You want to understand how to experiment in ways that'll help you improve your experience, and how you can use these to better it all. When you're engaging in tantra, you should always focus on experimenting with this and work on trying to improve your own personal health and wellness too. This will in turn definitely make it fun and try out new things. Trying new things can change you, and it'll also enhance your experience by a lot.

Tantra is a very in-depth and personal experience and understanding what it is that you're doing with your partner is ideal, and it can, in turn, change you. This alone will help you learn more about your partner and building that own connection that you have with them to something bigger, and better than ever before.

Five Tantric Sex positions you need to try

When it comes to tantric sex positions, there are a few things that you want out of them. First, you want something that heightens intimacy. You also want something that lets you maintain eye contact with the other person. Finally, you want something that lets you go slow and not unfocused, so a position like doggy style, for example, is probably not ideal for those of us who like to have tantric sex.

So, what does that leave us? Well, a lot actually. While most people try to avoid missionary sex, there are other positions that you can use, and a lot that you'll benefit from if you're looking for fun and spicy tantric sex positions.

The Passion Pretzel

This is one that's a bit interesting for those of us who usually have sex with our feet either both on the ground or extended out against a surface. This s a very hot and erotic position, however, and again, simple to do.

The instructions are simple. You want to kneel with both of you facing one another, and what you want to do, is you take the opposite foot of the other person and place it on the ground flat and start to move closer. So, for example, if your partner has their left leg up you go with your right. From there, you want to slowly move closer, letting your genitalia touch one another. Then, you want to lean forward on both of your feet, and then, you want to lunge back, and both of you start to do this.

Now, this is a great one if you want to experience the slow, meditative aspects of tantra. That's because both of you will assume the exact same stance, and both of you will share control as you do this. It's one that lets you go slow, and exact with the way you do it. Since you both have your arms available, ed your mouths too, think of all of the different places that you can go with this. This is a great one for great stimulation of your genitalia, and for those that like clitoral contact and the higher ascent to a climatic state, this is a great way to do it. It might not bring about orgasm, but for those of us who want to feel the effects of the more meditative aspects of tantra, then this is how you do it. It's simple, effective, and lets you feel the climactic nature of the different sensations, and it's a great way to experience the equality of this and makes you feel amazing as well.

The mermaid

This is one that's wonderful for both of you if you want to experience the fun friction of sex, but also take it in a way that's slow and steady. What you want to do, is have the receiver lay faceup against the edge of the countertop, bed, or desk. You can from there place the pillow underneath your butt for some elevation. From there, extend your legs up, keeping them together, and you can put your hands underneath the pillow in order to raise your pelvis much higher, and then use them to hold the desk or counter for some leverage. Or, you can keep them free and then stimulate your partner. From there your partner proceeds to enter you while they stand up, whether it be on a bed, desk, or whatever, and they can use your feet to grip this for leverage, which is a great way to give stability.

Now this one is a part of tantra because you can have intimate moments facing one another, and remember, your hands are free. If your partner needs to use the legs that's near them for support, use that, but the idea behind this is actually the full, simulating sensation that lets you have blissful friction and a very tight fit. This is a great way to really connect with your partner, and it also allows for clitoral stimulation too. Just remember not to rush this, and your partner can, if they really want to, tease and stimulate your breasts and other locations as they thrust into you, and it will, in turn, create a stimulating and exciting experience in the realm of tantra.

Torrid Tidal wave

This is a great one that is pretty hot, and it allows you to experience the fun, tantric nature of sex, and it's good for both light penetration and also for a bit of stimulation between both of you.

This is a great pose for pretty much any make-out session that's happening whether it be on a bed, or even just lying about together. This is a great one for you to do as well, to begin with. The man should be on the bottom, with his legs together and straight. The woman will then straddle the penis, and from there stretch out so that you're on top, and your pelvises are lined up. Rest your weight on your hands by bringing your torso up. This one isn't as spicy and hot as say, other types of sex positions, but this is a great one for stimulation and is perfect for tantric sex because there is a lot of great stimulation to this as well. With every touch and pull, the clitoris does rub against the pelvic bones, creating friction that's practically toe-clenching and it creates that deep, passionate stimulation that you won't get anywhere else.

The Lap Dance

This is another good one especially if you're in a space such as a chair that's tall and backed, such as one that's on a desk or table, and one that's strong enough to hold your bodies. I like to do this one on the couch or armchair too since it holds weigh pretty well.

Pad this down, and have the man sit down on the bottom. Have the woman straddle the man and then lean back a little bit, placing hands on knees as well. From there, extend the legs with one at a time, until the angles are resting on the shoulders too. The woman is mostly in control of this, and you can pump the booty back and forth at a speed that will be amazing, and make you moan. You can balance the weight between hands and ankles, and the guy can hold you as well as you do this.

It's a very hot position, and it definitely provides a very erotic point of view.

How To Talk Dirty In An Erotic Way

When it comes to talking erotically with your partner, there is a certain level of intimacy that must be achieved. This intimacy is very important, because otherwise, your words will fall flat, and will be deemed almost ridiculous in a way. You have to set the mood, and make sure that you maintain it as well. There are several ways you can do this, but you cannot set the mood without first gaining confidence.

Why is Confidence Important?

If you do not have confidence, it can bring an air of uncertainty to your bedroom endeavors. This is something that you would find yourself struggling to overcome. First impressions are everything, and if you are not confident the first time you try to introduce erotic conversation, you could turn your partner off from it for a long time.

Confidence is the foundation for anything in life. If you want to achieve any of your goals, confidence will get your farther than even knowledge, because you will not constantly second guess yourself. Doing this can lead to many different mistakes that will cause you possibly to not achieve your goal. It is essential that you have confidence when you are trying to dirty talk. It will make your words appear to come out effortlessly, and to help you encourage your partner to join in. When you seem confident, your partner will use your confidence to help build theirs.

Confidence is sexy. It is the drive behind what gets the libido up and running. You have to be able to have confidence for dirty talk, because it is all about being sexy, and you cannot pull off sexy without confidence. No confidence means an ineffective attempt at wooing your partner with words.

Life becomes easier to handle. The less you try to tear yourself down, the more you love yourself. This makes it easier to face every day, because you are not your own worst enemy. When you genuinely believe in yourself, you can find a lot more to enjoy in life. This makes life a lot easier to look forward to.

You won't rely on outside validation. The most attractive quality in a person is their ability to be sure of themselves. These people do not need validation from others, and find themselves quite appealing in their own rights. They feel this way without being overtly cocky, and they have a great balance of self-assurance.

You will not be afraid of the good things in life. By not being afraid of these things, you will be less likely to sabotage your attempts to find happiness, because you will know that you deserve them. This helps in relationships, because you will not try to push the other person away, and will want to bring them closer. You will be confident when you find the right person, and will want to show them the real you, rather than trying to get them to tell you who to be.

Why Might Confidence Be Lacking?

Some people just seem to ooze confidence in everything that they do. They feel as if they are meant to do whatever it is they set their mind to. When they go for something, it just seems to fall in their lap. You may not have this much confidence, and that is okay. The important question is why you feel that way.

Insecurities run rampant in the world. Some people are told from a young age that they are not good enough, and it is engrained in their mind. For some people, the entire world could tell them that they are good enough, but it just takes one trusted person to tell them that they aren't to wreck their self-confidence. Whatever the reason, not having confidence can mean disaster for you.

Some people seem to feel like they must be perfect at everything, including looks to have confidence. This is not the truth. No one is perfect at everything, and trying to be can leave you a nervous wreck. This is not a good way to introduce dirty talk. You must go in having confidence in order to cover up any words that may not have been phrased properly. You must have confidence so that you are not dissuaded when it doesn't go perfectly, because there will be those days.

Confidence is something that not everyone has naturally, and that is okay. There is a way to build your confidence, even if you do not seem to have any. You just have to make sure that you follow through with all of these steps. When you are trying to build your confidence, it is key to remember that it does not always happen in one day, and you have to work hard at it, and on yourself as well. You cannot give up just because you do not find yourself the best in the world after trying for a day or two to build your confidence. It does not work like that, and that can cause a lot of people to give up, because they want the easy way out.

Giving up would be social torture to yourself. You have to keep working on it in order to make yourself a better person, and a better partner. No one wants to constantly have to reassure their partner that they find them attractive and sexy. You have to be able to assure yourself, because you want people to want you, not feel like they have to want you.

If you give up, you could find yourself in a bit of a tough spot, and not able to achieve what you wanted to achieve in your goals of becoming a more open person in the bedroom. You must have confidence.

The Steps to Gaining Confidence

Confidence generally takes some work, so do not worry if you are not the most confident person in the world. You can learn how to gain confidence in yourself with these steps. These steps are designed to help even the most self-conscious gain enough confidence to be more adventurous in the bedroom.

The first step to gaining confidence is to simply fake it. That's right, pretending that you have confidence will eventually trick your brain into thinking that you really are confident. This will make it easier to build up your real confidence. When you fake confidence, it will have other people noticing that you seem surer of yourself. This validation will show you that it really works. When you look good, you feel better, and that is the mentality that faking it uses. It may seem silly, but "fake it till you make it" is not a saying for no reason. It applies here too. Faking it does not necessarily mean acting like the jock in a cheesy nineties movie, it simply means believing in yourself a little more, or at least acting like you do.

Setting the mood

It is important to set the mood with your partner. You have to make sure that you are making them comfortable, and turning them on at the same time.

There are several things that you can do to set the mood. The first is communication.

Communication

Communication will open the door to being able to dirty talk your partner. If you can communicate about anything with your partner, you will be able to set the mood a lot easier, because you can both talk about whether it is the right time to engage in sexual conversation. If you are not able to communicate, sometimes one of you may not be in the mood, and setting the mood will be futile, because it will feel forced.

It is true. Communication is the key to any successful relationship. Especially when it comes to something like Kamasutra. It is the duty of each partner to ensure that they are satisfying their lover, but it is also their duty to let their lover know how they are feeling.

Humans are not mind readers, and often do not know what you are thinking. You have to be open with your partner, and allow your partner to be open with you, otherwise you will have some serious issues. A lot of times people are not open because their partners shut them down, and get angry at criticism, so they feel that they are not able to be open. You have to encourage communication both in and out of the bedroom.

In the bedroom, make your partner feel comfortable with vocalization. If they are nervous let them know that it is not silly, and you like knowing that what you are doing feels good, or if it doesn't feel good, you want to know so that you can make the proper adjustments. You should also lead by example. A lot of times one partner is very vocal, while the other is silent, you should both be vocal. Do not be afraid of shouting or screaming in pleasure. Also, do not be afraid to tell your partner what doesn't feel good. You can make it less harsh by asking them to change something nicely, rather than saying that hurts. This way there is no killing of the mood.

You also need communication in your everyday life as well. When your partner upsets you, you should tell them rather than bottling it up until it becomes a fight. You should also tell them if they are doing something you like. Too many times in the real world, everyone talks about what they don't like, but no one talks about what they do like. Yet in the bedroom it is the opposite. You should definitely find a balance in both.

Communication is a necessary part of your everyday life. Even if it is just talking about your day. Many relationships fail because there is not enough communication to keep the passion alive. You want to tell your partner everything. When they ask how your day was, it is because they want to know. The do not want a one word answer such as "good." When they ask you, be free with the information. Tell them every little boring detail, and then ask them about their day. Revel in what they are saying to you, even if the words are unimportant. Your lover will be happy knowing that even if they had a really boring day, you want to know about it. Things like that are the little things that make the world go round, and truly make a relationship work. Communication is a show of love, and it will help keep your love strong. Use it to its fullest power.

Making Your Partner Comfortable

The biggest way to get your partner comfortable is communication. However, there is one other thing you can do to help get in the mood. Make them feel good about themselves. Help boost your partner's self-confidence. This will help relax them and allow them to relax knowing you find them as attractive as they feel they need to be to reciprocate. To do this, you simply have to compliment them.

Compliment Them

A lot of the time, being self-conscious is a big problem. People are so caught up in self-image that it is hard to be confident in your own skin. A lot of that has to do with the way bodies are portrayed in the media. The world has this idea of perfection, and expects everyone to reach it. Even if your partner does not say it out loud, chances are, they have a poor self-image. Everyone struggles with some form of insecurity, and there are not enough compliments going around in the world these days.

Find five things about your partner that you like visually, and five things about them that you like outside of their physical appearance. Throughout the day, compliment them on these things. Make sure they understand that your compliments are sincere. It is best to look them in the eyes when you compliment them. Compliments will make them feel like they are on top of the world.

Do not overdo the compliments though, because they can begin to feel insincere. Make them heartfelt and true. Do not use them just for getting ready for sex. You should be complimenting your partner on a regular basis. Build up their self-esteem so that they feel like they are powerful. You may be surprised at the wild side they could unleash when they feel like they are truly good for you. It is quite the sight to behold.

Setting the mood will help set the stage for intimate conversation. You want to have the right mood when you are trying to get your partner to feel comfortable. There is no specific time when setting the mood is good, however, there is a setting where it is.

When to Set the Mood

If you and your partner are looking to start into something in the evening, do not wait until just before you hit the bedroom to set the mood. Use the entire day, even when you are at work. You can text your partner throughout the day little things that will get their motor running, and make them more ready and open to converse with you sexually.

When you are trying to set the mood, you can engage in dirty talk then, starting at a mild level, and then going up from there as the day transcends.

Getting in the Mood

How to Get Him in the Mood

Although your man could not take his hands off you when you first met, he might seem not in the mood after a while. He might get distracted once in a while and look somehow off, hence the need for you to get him in the mood. Despite the fact that most men easily get in the mood for sex, yours might seem a bit off on some days.

These tips should help you get him back in the mood for hot sexual sessions:

Prepare Him Bubble Bath

When your man comes back home from work after a long day's work, you can welcome him with a candle-lit bubble bath scented with vanilla. Various studies indicate that men get aroused the most by the smell of vanilla. You can take it a notch higher by waiting for him naked in the tab with two glasses of wine.

Give Him a Sensual Massage

You can give him a sensual massage to arouse his feelings and get him in the mood. Use things like fluffy wool or feathers or silky scarves to gently flip all over his body. Cinnamon scented candle and massage oils like frankincense and lavender are perfect for the sensual massage session. You can add more vigor to the massage by blindfolding your man.

Whisper Sexy Words in His Ears

When around him, whisper sexy words in his ears while letting him feel your deep breaths. You can also leave him a sexy voice message in your sexiest voice.

Look Him Directly in the Eyes

Enhance intimacy and arouse your man by staring directly into his eyes; do not blink or break your gaze. Well, don't just stare at him; use lustful eyes to lock your eyes with his and you will see how turned on he is. Men go crazy at the thought of a horny woman. If you could tell him that you are not wearing anything down there, his lust for you will go on overdrive.

Sing Him a Love Song

Choose one of your man's favorite love songs that you also like. Record yourself singing it and save it on a CD. Leave it on his car seat so he can find it in the morning as he leaves for work. When he gets to listen to it, he won't stop thinking about you throughout the day. He will be eager to come back home and share good intimate moments with you.

Express Your Feelings through Poetry

Write either a traditional or naughty poem about what you love about your man, your love life or even the first time you met. Leave it somewhere open where he will find it, or just read it to him. You can do the reading in bed.

Find the Way to His Heart

They say one of the ways to a man's heart is through good food. Prepare his favorite dish and place a sexy note next to the serving, letting him know your expectations of him later in the evening or night.

Give Him Flowers

According to a certain study conducted by the University of Rutgers, most men love receiving flowers, it increases their happiness and interactions socially. Choose his favorite colors or send him a bouquet of blue, red and purple flowers with the scents he loves most. Deliver the flowers with a sexy note.

Buy Him a Gift

Surprise your man with a gift you are sure he will love. You can also ask him to accompany you to a lingerie store and help you select something that he would love to see you wear.

Share a Bar of Chocolate

Studies associate chocolate with less depression and loneliness in men. You can also choose a menu that features chocolates to share with your man. There are several online that you can try.

Deep throat Him

Your man will definitely love the feeling of his penis deep in your throat. You can start by sucking his not erect penis until it is hard before you can deep-throat him. If this is something you cannot do, you can give him a visual effect by deep throating a toy penis.

Shave or Wax for Him

Men love the soft feel of smooth skin. Rub his penis gently against rough areas of your skin and slowly move to the smooth shaven or waxed areas so he can feel the difference in touch. You should do this firmly and lightly until he is so hard that he begs to feel the warmth of your vagina.

Nibble the Back of His Neck

Arouse the sexual desire in your man by nibbling the back of his neck using your tongue. Letting him feel your deep breaths is a plus.

Give Him a Spicy Kiss

Apply a spicy lipstick on your lips before kissing your man. It will spice up your oral sex sessions. He will get stimulated while you enjoy using your hot lips on him.

Rub His Penis

Gently hold your man's penis with your fingers and gently rub him. You can apply some lotion or gel to reduce friction and facilitate the arousal.

Get him to dress you

A horny man is a very creative one and will spend any amount of money to get his sexual fantasies met. Give your man a chance to dress you from head to toe for an entire week and see what happens. Let him do the shopping for the stuff that he wants you to wear. He will love it when you follow what he says. And the thought that you are wearing the clothes that he bought you will make him want you even the more. He will be looking forward for a wonderful session when he sees you.

Make the First Move

When you know he is about to get home, get naked and spread yourself on the bed waiting for him. His first sight of you will definitely arouse him and get him in the mood. You can also take the first step during other times, for instance, when you are relaxing in the living room over the weekend. You can move closer to him and start kissing him; he will definitely respond. Just ensure that he is in a good mood before making the move.

You can also undress him and push him onto the bed before you take charge and do the riding. You can also give him a quickie, look good for him, give him blowjobs, spank his butt, get him ready from the moment he wakes up, and stimulate his senses to get him in the mood.

How to Get Her In The Mood

According to two psychology professors at the Texas University and co-authors of the book 'Why Women Have Sex: Understanding Sexual Motivations from Adventure to Revenge', women need to be inspired in order to get in the mood for sex, whereas men are up for it anywhere and anytime, irrespective of the prevailing situation.

Men often wish that their women would respond more to their sexual gestures, or even initiate sex more. This difference is attributed to the fact that women's desire for sex depends on their immediate environment in terms of response and variance. Women experience sex in both their bodies and minds; men, on the other hand, focus more on their genitals.

Men are compared to firemen, who are ready to have sex anytime because to them, it is an emergency. Women, however, are exciting just like fire; the surrounding conditions must be right for them to fire up, let alone keep burning.

Your woman wants to have sex only when she thinks it is worth it. Therefore, you need to motivate your wife or girlfriend, for them to see sex as an exciting priority. Here are some ways to help you get her in the mood:

Give Her Mild Bondage

Your woman can be turned on by the mere thought that you are entirely responsible for her satisfaction sexually. You can get her ready by sending her an email or leaving a voice message or note earlier in the day. Tell her to put on some make up and wear your favorite outfit.

If you love a submissive woman, you can order her to submit to you by getting her on her knees and being your 'slave' just for the moment. Be her master and order her to do what you want. You can also use a gentle item to tie her as bondage and use a tickler or feather to arouse her.

You can also opt for gentle bondage sex toys or just spank her lightly using your hand. Note that the aim of the bondage is to bring your woman pleasure so that she can climax; no kind of pain or humiliation should be involved.

Role Play

You can ask her to role play her fantasy or be the slut you always yearn for. You can ask her to play the role of a stripper and give you one of a kind shows. If she is okay with having a camera around, you can decide to record the show for future use and reference.

Make Her Mind Sex

For women, sex starts in the mind. Your woman cannot think of having sex with you if she has other things occupying her mind. Tell her what you want to do to her in advance in detail. When together, rub your hands against her body and kiss her shoulders up her neck.

Remove her panties with her clothes on and slip your hand beneath her dress or top to tease her nipples. You can use the other hand to gently touch and rub her butt. You can let her arouse herself as you watch by rubbing her clit; let her sit on a chair with legs apart.

You can ask her to describe how she feels and before you know it, she will be begging you to do that to her, but with your hard penis deep inside her vagina.

Explore Her Fantasies

You can ask your woman to give you details of her sexual fantasies. By just sharing that kind of information with you, she will automatically get aroused. However, you need to prepare for the unexpected as her fantasy or what turns her on might make you insecure; there is no need for that.

Take advantage of that opportunity for your own gain. You can tell her story that matches her fantasy as you caress and kiss her gently. Whisper softly in her ears and let her imagination be her only limitation. If she responds to it, you can be sure that she is getting wet as well.

Watch Passionate Porn Together

Unlike men, women prefer aural porn. Find a suitable one with a sexy storyline and enjoy listening together. A passionate visual erotica would do though if you can find one. As you get aroused watching or listening to your favorite erotica, you can run your hands inside her clothes for greater arousal and pleasure.

Make Compliments

Women love compliments mainly because they are more self-conscious regarding their nude bodies and easily get insecure than their male counterparts. You need to make your woman feel secure in order to get her in the mood.

As you caress her body and give her hot kisses, tell her that you find her attractive, what you like most about her body, and how much she turns you on; and, you just can't keep your hands and tongue off her body. The more specific your compliments about her are the better.

You can tell her you love her soft skin, warm smile, beautiful shape or even size, and the soft feel of her firm breasts. Actually, the more you compliment her daily, the more she will always be in the mood.

Caress Her Sensually

You can easily get your woman in the mood by simply giving her tender strokes of your touches all over her body. As you touch her, your aim is to get her aroused for intercourse. Use long gentle caresses to massage her breasts and touch her all over. You can also move your hands down her body and put your hand in her panties to gently rub her clit.

Maintain the slow tempo throughout until she is totally aroused. Only then can you play rough, as she would be asking for.

Prolong the Foreplay

Foreplay means the world to women. Do not just rip off her panties and expect her to let you penetrate. You need to engage her in prolonged foreplay before you can make love to her. Hold her close, stroke her hair, touch her face, look directly into her eyes, kiss her soft spots, caress her body, and even kiss her neck.

You can also give her a sensual massage as part of foreplay to arouse her properly. The gentle touch of your fingertips all over her body, commonly known as 'spider legs' can get your woman really wet, ready for intercourse.

Create a Good Ambience

The right ambience to a woman is as good as being in the mood. You need to ensure that the ambience is stress-free, has proper lighting, is quiet, and if possible, smells great. The environment should also be clean because your woman will definitely love that.

It is easier for you to get her in the mood if the ambience is good because it relaxes and calms her mind to focus only on the feelings you are trying to arouse in her.

Rules of the Game

Rule 1: Welcome Back to Virginity

In every way that really matters, each couple setting out on The Sex Bucket List must be unadulterated, honest virgins!

Imagine (or grasp) that you are fresh out of the plastic new to the sex game.

You've never been given a climax You've never contacted your accomplice explicitly You've never at any point taken your accomplices garments off in the warmth of the minute That implies, you can't experience the rundown check off filthy things that you've just done... in light of the fact that recall that, you're authoritatively virgins (once more).

Rule 2: Take Turns Choosing your Sexy Challe

Ladies first, men second. The lady picks ANY provocative pail list challenge that turns her on and her accomplice must withstand. At that point, it's the man's turn.

Much the same as foreplay, you don't need to experience this sex container list in any specific request. Let your sex drive do the picking. At the point when an insidious opportunity presents itself or you get a specific desire to play out a dream – pull out all the stops.

Rule 3: "Game On"

Some Bucket List difficulties happen normally, similar to the lady starting morning sex or the man twisting his woman over in the shower. While others, like dream play or telephone sex, can require some correspondence of what precisely is going to occur.

At the point when it's your chance to pick a devious demonstration that requires a common comprehension, and you know precisely what you need, utilize the words "Game On" to tell your accomplice that it's playtime.

These enchantment words signal that you're going to check off a sex challenge, regardless of whether it pretends or areola cinches. You can content this code to your accomplice on your path home from work, you can murmur it in their ear as your hand slides down their jeans or can pass these words over the table on a bit of paper as you advance toward the restroom for a few enthusiastic open sexes.

Rule 4: No Double Dipping on Challenges Marked with "xxx"

At the point when you see "xxx" by a Bucket List challenge, this implies there must be at any rate 1 hour between the consummation of one sex challenge and the picking of the following.

This, my companions, is called Delayed Sexual Gratification.

A portion of these difficulties are intended to leave you asking for additional. You are intended to replay that hot make-out meeting again and again in your mind at work. What's more, you should need to surge home just to tear your accomplice's garments off. Realizing that your better half is kicking the bucket to have you is absolutely precious.

Along these lines, practice a little discretion... it will make your climaxes 10x as solid.

Rule 5: Temporary Pass

Possibly the Queen isn't prepared to have her can play with today around evening time... or the Lord isn't prepared to have he can play with. Every challenger is permitted 3 transitory passes, where the picking accomplice must pick another challenge for the present. You can return to the skipped challenge at a later date.

Rule 6: Swap and Combine Challenges

On the off chance that there is a test that you two completely concur isn't something, you wish to seek after... like engaging in sexual relations in a parking area... at that point swap it. With what? A blend of 2 difficulties. For instance.

Engage in sexual relations on in a parking area Engage in sexual relations on the kitchen table Give him a penis massage Your new test could be to... give him a penis massage on the kitchen table.

Get it? You should finish an aggregate of 100 difficulties before the finish of the rundown.

No cheating and no skipping!

Rule 7: Push your Limits

Sexual edification lies directly outside of your sensual safe place. You're going to require a receptive outlook and an eagerness to be defenseless.

Obviously, having a trio is harrowing... but on the other hand, it's screwing great. Start moderate and stir your way up to the difficulties that push you the most. Play by an "On the off chance that you never attempt, you'll never know" mindset and simply go with it.

In the case of something feels awkward, chuckle about it together. Bond over it together.

On this note, a piggyback principle to #6 ... you may just swap a sum of 4 challenges. Not 4 difficulties each, however 4 difficulties complete. In the case of something feels odd and awkward, tell your accomplice "Hello, this feels peculiar and awkward. Help me through this one". The general purpose is to develop together and push your breaking points together.

Follow along. Keep Pace.

The most ideal approach to monitor your Sex Bucket List Challenge is with 2 highlighters. At the point when you finish, check every erratic the rundown.

◇ Assign 1 highlighter as the "I need to do this once more" shading

◇ Assign 1 highlighter as "Not my top pick" action shading What's more, for those "Unsure yet I'm willing to attempt it once more"

◇ exercises, circle it and return to it once you've wrapped up the rundown.

Keep pace by doing, in any event, 4 difficulties for each week. The objective is to go into an exceptional sexual retreat with your accomplice

– not a periodic bare movement when you have time. Before the finish of the rundown, you'll have changed your ordinary workweek into an energizing, energy-filled sex fest.

At the end of the day, don't take a year to finish this rundown! You'll lose all energy.

The Sex Bucket List Pact

Your first test begins now.

Snatch every others' butts, investigate every others' eyes and state, "We will get unusual in any event 4 times each week until this rundown is done".

Let's assume it once again. Was that abnormal? Great. Things are going to get a ton more bizarre. Your first attractive experience begins now.

Keep in mind, you don't need to go all together. Let your moxie do the picking...

Part 1: Virgin Territory

Do you recollect past times worth remembering of waiting for foreplay? The days when you were all the while clutching your virginity and investigating your sexuality for hours one after another... over the garments? We're returning it to the rudiments.

1. Dry Hump–xxx

Try not to think little of how hot and hot this guiltless little bother can be.

Jump over your accomplice and start gradually kissing their neck and snacking on their ear while you gradually start to crush on their lap. This will advance into an all-out make out meeting with a hard chicken and wet undies.

The standard: no sex and nothing underneath the garments. You must leave like great little virgins.

2. Let Her Watch

Give yourself handwork while she watches. She isn't permitted to kiss you, to contact herself or to contact you. This is a limited show.

3. Let Him Watch

Lay back and satisfy yourself simply like you would alone. Do whatever it is that turns you on and let him figure out how you like to be contacted and what carries you to climax.

Same principles as above.

4. Make Out for 20 Minutes (Hands in Neutral Territory)- xxx

Rediscover what it feels like to kiss your band together with no closure objective. There is no race to detach every others' garments or convey the circumstance to the room.

Simply recollect what it feels like to truly want one another and speak with just your tongues.

5. Make Out for 15 Minutes(Touch Each Other Over the Clothes)- xxx

Kiss each other as enthusiastically as you'd like and let your hands cooperate.

Squeeze her areolas and snatch her can. Rub on that hard lump in his jeans and let him rub you through your underwear. What's more, much the same as in the past... leave. As the standards direct, you can finish a subsequent basin list challenge in one hour after you complete the process of making out.

6. Sext

Throughout the day. While you're both grinding away or school, send each other filthy messages specifying what you will do to one another once you get home.

7. Tease Your Partner with SexyPhotos #SendNudes

The two people are visual animals! Send your darling an attractive photograph of yourself in the exercise center storage space with those tight game bra titties or a photograph of all of you wet right out of the shower. It's everything about points!

8. Give Him a Hand Job

The way into decent handwork is bunches of lube, regardless of whether that be KY Lube, Coconut Oil or spit and salivation – get that infant wet. Request that your man appears you how he prefers it OR bothers him until he completely can't stand it any longer furthermore, is imploring you to make him cum.

The Rules: You can't utilize your mouth and he can't complete himself.

9. Make Her Cum with Just your hands

A lady's vagina resembles a mix lock; everyone requires an alternate code to get to the products. Discover that code!

Possibly she enjoys 2 fingers entering her or she may adore you just scouring her with your fingers. Work it out and don't be hesitant to animate her areolas with your free hand if that is the stuff to get her there.

10. Phone Sex

Anyplace, whenever. Call your accomplice while they are busy working and start speaking profanely or call them while they're at a social capacity and let them know what you're doing to your body at that point. To be clear with respect to what is going on... don't be reluctant to utilize the enchantment words – "Game On".

11. Cyber Sex

Whenever both of you are isolated, regardless of whether that be in various urban areas or in various rooms – compensate for the separation with a little digital bother.

Facetime or Skype as you contact one another, speaking profanely and portraying what you need to do to your sweetheart's body. Garments might be shed, toys may be utilized, and full-on climaxes might be had.

12. Titty Fuck

We should expect that you both are extra horny virgins with a creative mind, will we?

Folks, slide your chicken in the middle of those two excellent bosoms and delight yourself. Young ladies have a go at scouring your areolas simultaneously to truly get in the soul.

This game isn't only for Double D's! On the off chance that you don't have a tit valley to work with. Handwork while scouring the tip of his penis all over your areolas will work, as well. Keep in mind: lube is your companion.

13. Mutual Stimulation

The more turned on she is, the more love she places into that handwork. The more smoking his handwork is, the more enthusiastically those fingers are going to finger that wonderful pussy. Try not to squeeze each other to cum, simply appreciate the ride and see where it takes you.

14. Suck Toes

There are focuses on your feet and toes that are legitimately associated with your attractive spots. You'd be astounded how strongly a little blameless toe sucking can turn you on. Attempt this movement for 5 minutes. In case you're getting a charge out of it, keep going.

Attractive Tip: To flavor this one up, start with certain leggings or socks on his or her feet and gradually strip them off.

Part 2: Everything Oral

Oral in bed is acceptable, oral on the kitchen counter is far and away superior. Just by tweaking a couple of factors like the spot and the position, you can make a spic and span sexual experience for both of you.

15. Go Down on Her Until Orgasm

Eating a lady's pussy resembles an Olympic game. Each game takes practice also, commitment, much the same as a lady's stunning vagina. Making a lady cum with your tongue takes the perfect measure of weight, speed, and time. You may think you comprehend what your lady likes, yet it's a great opportunity to find a few new problem areas.

Lick her in new places and ask her what feels better. Does she need you to go higher? Quicker? Tune in to the manner in which she groans. Quiet may mean "switch things up". Focus on how her body reacts and you'll be capable to give her that full-body climax.

Ace Tip: Most men don't have the foggiest idea about this, however here and there a lady's failure to cum from her accomplice giving her cunnilingus is that we stress that we're taking excessively long or that our accomplice isn't getting a charge out of it. Along these lines, this test is particularly for the young ladies who are too sacrificial to even consider letting themselves lay back and appreciate. Realizing that you're not going to quit licking her until she cums will get her out of her head and into the occasion.

16. Give Him a Blow Job

Cumming from oral and cumming from sex are 2 entirely unexpected encounters. Treat your man to an unwinding and sexy BJ anyway you like it. Play with that chicken in new manners. Lick it, spit on it, slap it against your tongue, rub it all the rage. Truly make this blowie your own.

17. Ride His Face

There are two very hot approaches to ride your man's tongue. One: Sit all over and cover him with your entirely pussy. He'll adore it.

Try not to be reluctant to delicately ride him to and fro, giving his tongue a little bit of consolation. Even better, have something strong to clutch. This will give permit you more control.

Two Have him jump on his knees while you put one decisive advantage over the kitchen counter or work area. This will give him full access to all the enjoyment territories. He can likewise utilize his hands to move you exactly how he prefers.

18. Sixty-Nine

A man lying on his back, Woman straddling his face while his rooster is splendidly situated for her to play with.

Women, you can utilize your hands and your mouth here. Men of their word, you can utilize your hands to move her to and fro all over for a few additional incitements.

19. Blow Job Under the Table

While he's having his morning espresso at the table or in supper, nimbly slide under the table and unfasten his jeans. The rest is up to you what's more, your mouth. Have fun down there.

20. Sweet Cunnilingus

Chocolate Syrup, Ice Cream, Frosting – it's the ideal opportunity for dessert.

Here's the test: totally spread her quite pussy in the delectable treat of your decision. You're going to lick every last bit of it up until she comes. Try not to be hesitant to make a wreck. The best oral is constantly chaotic.

21. The Lollipop Blow Job

Prepared to get clingy?

Before you begin sucking on him, begin sucking on candy while you get him began with your other hand. Watching you lick that sucker will get him quickly hard. After you've prodded him enough, utilize the entirety of that extra spit and clingy squeeze in your mouth to give him the most delectable penis massage ever – simply don't put that candy down. Stop on occasion to suck a little more, spit a portion of those juices all over his rooster, and bother him while he asks for you to wrap up.

22. Blindfolded Blow Job

Utilize a tie or purchase a pleasant silk eye veil for your lady to give you a blindfolded head. Without her sight, she'll utilize every last bit of her different faculties to truly get into it as she feels and tastes her route all over your chicken.

23. No Moving Allowed

We as a whole need to cum! For the most part, when somebody is giving us orally, we are attempting to make ourselves cum. Be that as it may, the climaxes are so a lot more grounded when you simply let them occur. In this way, here's the standard: While you go down on your accomplice, they aren't permitted to move. Not their hands or their hips. Each time they move, you quit sucking or licking. They will be compelled to lay back and let that climax assume control over their whole body.

24. Lick His Nipples

Areola play isn't only for ladies. A few men have extremely delicate areolas that carry them to climax... and a few men don't. You'll never know until you attempt.

Lick with a delicate tongue, lick with a solid tongue, squeeze, and chomp. Attempt everything to perceive what works and what doesn't. Give it a couple of moments before you surrender.

25. Swallow

For a man, having the tip of his penis licked and sucked from the very starting as far as possible of a knock work is completely socks off blowing. Let him finish in your mouth and it will resemble the Christmas of oral sex.

Sexual Fantasies

A sexual fantasy is something that a person imagines or dreams of doing or taking part in, in a sexual context. This fantasy is something that, when imagined, leads the person to become sexually aroused. A sexual fantasy will commonly involve something that you would not regularly have the chance to do. For example, it could be something like having sex with a jail guard as their inmate. In this case, this is not something that you would likely do, but you fantasize about doing it as it arouses you.

Common Sexual Fantasies

Sexual fantasies often come in the form of role play. Like the example above, a sexual fantasy often needs to be acted out, such as one person playing the role of the jail guard and the other playing the part of the inmate. This is a common sexual fantasy, and this brings us to the first category of sexual fantasies.

1. Power Dynamic Fantasies

Many fantasies and role plays involve some type of power dynamic, where one person has control over the other or is in an authoritative role, while their partner is submissive to them.

2. Kink

Another common type of sexual fantasy involves kink. This can include things like restricted movement from being tied up, being spanked or spanking their partner, or having sex wearing specific things like leather or fur.

3. Fetishes

The final category that we will look at involves fetishes. This can be something like fantasizing about having someone suck on your toes, fantasizing about peeing on someone or having them pee on you, wishing to have sex in a large group, or wanting to have sex with a mask on.

As I'm sure you can see, the different categories of sexual fantasies involve a lot of overlap, which. Is why they are most often referred to as the general umbrella of "sexual fantasies."

Best Sexual Fantasies for Beginners Who Want to Try New Things

Now that you understand sexual fantasies, I am going to share some common sexual fantasies that are great for beginners who are looking to spice up their sex life a little bit.

The Photo Shoot

The first example of a sexual fantasy comes in the form of a role play. This role play is The Photo Shoot role play. In this role play, one person will play the model, and one person will play the photographer. You can begin acting out how a regular photoshoot would go, with one person posing for photos clothed in front of the camera. The photographer can tell the model what poses they want to see. As it progresses, the photographer can tell the model to take off some items of clothing, or the model can do this on their own. As they take more layers of clothing off, the photographer can ask them to do more and more sensual positions for the camera. Eventually, the photographer can go in to help them get undressed, or when they are fully naked, the photographer can step in to help the model move their body into poses they want to see. With the touch barrier broken, they can then continue to touch each other. The model can position themselves in positions with their legs spread, their but out their breasts towards the camera, anything. This will eventually progress to the photographer touching the model, and sex ensues.

Public Sex

Some sexual fantasies involve having sex in new or nerve-wracking locations. One example of this is public sex. This can involve having sex in a movie theatre, in an alleyway, in a boardroom of the office, and so on. Maybe you fantasize about this while having sex at home in your bedroom, or maybe you take it to the actual place that you fantasize about and try it for real!

Handcuffs/Tying Up

Handcuffs are a sexy and simple introduction to the world of restraint and domination that you have probably heard of before. This is a great place to start because the person being restricted can still express their desires and wishes for pleasure but the other person is ultimately in charge of what they choose to agree to and what they do not. Because both partners can still see and talk to each other, they can communicate throughout, telling the other person how to touch them and what they like. The fact that one partner is in control will be the thing that makes both of you go wild with desire.

A great way to have your partner discover and appreciate your body if you are insecure is through a massage. Not just any, but a blindfolded massage. You can make this a sexy exploration with the blindfold being almost BDSM-like, or leading up to something bigger, or you can keep it cute and loving, whichever style best suits you both. After setting the mood and taking your partner's clothes off, get them to blindfold you. Have them lie down in a comfortable position and begin gently exploring their bodies with your hands. You can use massage oil if you want but focus on the exploration. exploring their body without your sight will give you a new perspective of the body you thought you knew so well. You will be able to feel the details you overlooked for all these years, and once you discover them, you will have a new image in front of your eyes every time you look at them afterward. You can take turns doing this, having the partner that is being explored lying down and enjoying the sensations, or you can do it together at the same time if you wish. With both of you naked and blindfolded, get into a comfortable position that allows all of your arms to be free to move and leaves your body open. Lying down on your sides face-to-face is a good position for this, and you can switch sides partway through if you wish. To start out, focus on exploring each other with your hands and avoid focusing too heavily on any one part of their body, we want to discover it all. Take your time, though, and move gently. Once you have been doing this for a little, you can start to kiss each other, still blindfolded, and progress to wherever you want to go. All of these sensations will prove to be different when blindfolded. You will have a heightened physical sensation because your vision is not there. If you wish to have sex, try it blindfolded as well. Oral sex and penetrative sex with a blindfold will surely help you rediscover their body even further. As the woman, try giving your partner a handjob while blindfolded. You will feel all of the curves and nuances to his penis and see it in a new way, perhaps. As the man, give your partner a vulva massage and find her clitoris with your eyes covered. This will help you to find it ever after without even looking. Feel around gently and discover everything between her legs. Eventually, you can slip a finger inside of her and discover her spot and what it feels like. Even though you never actually see it, having a blindfold on will enhance your physical sensations in general, so touching inside of her will feel different than it does when you have your vision.

Best Sex Positions To Try If You Are Insecure

Hot Seat

This position is called The Hot Seat. This position is good for those who are insecure when it comes to sex or about their body since both people will be pressed together and will not have room to see each other. It is also great because the nature of this position only allows for grinding into each other, and not for vigorous humping.

The man sits upright on the edge of the bed with his legs hanging off and his feet on the floor. The woman sits down on his lap, facing away from him, and he slides his penis into her. The woman can shift her body around and see which angles feel the best for both of them. If the woman is comfortable, the man can reach around her and massage her nipples or play with her clitoris from this position as well, and he can kiss her neck and her back sensually. You can move as slow or as fast as you like in this position, and take it at the depth you like.

Best Sex Positions for Anxious Lovers

Tantric sex involves being in touch with one's feelings and breath- almost like a meditation of sorts. Tantric sex takes this idea and uses it in relation to sex. Sex with oneself or sex with a partner is done through a deep connection. You practice being connected to yourself and your deeper feelings in order to more easily feel your feelings and reach orgasm quicker and with more intensity. Tantric sex is so useful for couples, especially those who are more anxious. This practice allows you both to get in touch with your feelings and your bodies, as well as each other in a slow, quiet, and patient way. This is great for anxious lovers who need time to relax and connect before beginning sex. The position below is a staple of Tantric Sex and is ideal for beginners to Tantra.

The Yab-Yum Position

Get together in the Yab-Yum position. A staple position in Tantric sex and the position that everything begins from. The man sits down with his legs crossed. The woman sits on his lap, her legs wrapped around him. You can do this position at the headboard of your bed so that one of you can lean on it for support if need be. Getting together like this brings you close at every point of your body, from your eyes to your chest to your feet. From here, we can begin to connect deeper than ever before. Synchronize your breathing with each other. You can look into each other's eyes if you wish. Sync up the speed and depth of your breathing and make sure it's not too shallow or too quick. Relax into this with each other and let your feelings guide you. You can do this for some time and let the experience unfold. Try to get in tune with the feelings of your body and see if you are receiving anything from the other person in their energy or their breath.

How to Overcome Insecurities in the Bedroom

There are many reasons why a person may feel insecure in the bedroom. This can be because of their body image, their performance, or their ability to please their partner. Below are some ways to deal with these insecurities.

Communication is the key to a fulfilling and pleasurable sex life. Knowing what you and your partner like and dislike allow you to focus on the things you enjoy and leave the things you don't behind. Knowing this will help to greatly reduce your anxiety surrounding performance or being able to please tour partner adequately. With so many options for ways to pleasure each other, you don't want to waste time on the things that don't make you scream out in pleasure, and communication is the way!

During sex is an important time to check in with your partner to see how they are feeling, what they are liking, and what they want more of. While you are having sex, it is easiest to communicate using dirty talk so that you don't ruin the mood by coming off too serious or too concerned. In order to properly communicate while also playing into the mood of the moment, you can do so in a sexy way, using sexy language. You should tell each other what you like by saying, "oh yes, I like that" or "I like when you touch me like that" This lets the person know to do more of the same because this is what will get you to orgasm. By being aware of these things and being able to talk about them in the moment, it will help with your confidence in the bedroom and reduce your insecurities.

Cardiovascular exercise has been shown to increase blood flow, which in turn increases your positive feelings during sex as well as the sensations your partner will feel on his penis when he slides it into your engorged vagina. Improving your aerobic capacity makes it so that blood will have an easier time flowing to the genitals, as your body becomes more efficient at dispersing it. This means positive things for your orgasm as well as your partner's! In terms of sex drive, doing weight training has been shown to increase your sex drive, which is another factor that will positively affect your ability to orgasm. Another one of the countless benefits of exercise on your sex life is that it will make you feel more confident and positive about your body. This, in turn, will make you feel more confident in the bedroom, which will improve your mood, reduce your stress and anxiety, and make it so that you are more likely to reach orgasm.

How to Overcome Anxiety in the Bedroom

It is very common for people to have anxiety in the bedroom, especially around things like orgasm and performance. There are some ways that you can reduce your orgasm and performance anxiety in the bedroom.

Your choice of environment can make a big difference when it comes to whether or not you can reach orgasm. If you tend to be someone who has trouble reaching orgasm for whatever reason, these details of the environment, the location, and the time will be important for your experience. They will determine whether or not you will be able to get concentrated enough to orgasm. We will discuss several factors that contribute to whether or not your environment is conducive to your pleasure and your orgasm. The reason why the environment, time and location are of such importance is that being comfortable with all of these factors will allow you to focus on yourself, your pleasure and your orgasm without distraction.

The ambiance, the mood, and the lighting must be selected so that they are simple enough to allow for sex to be the focus while being special enough to evoke a sense of sexy mystery. The environment can be based on your personal preference, but the main factor to keep in mind is that it is free of distractions and comfortable enough for you to feel relaxed. This leads us to the choice of location. The location choice is important for getting you in the mood and allowing you to stay in the mood. There are some things to keep in mind when selecting a location. You will want to select a location that allows both of you to relax, move around freely, and that will be free of concerns such as cleanliness, temperature, and physical comfortability.

The Importance Of Foreplay

Welcome to a crucial lesson of sex. I am aware that this topic has been dealt with before but I figured some more light could be shed in this regard.

The most common mistake an average man makes during the period of sex life is neglecting the importance of a good session of foreplay. A foreplay session is supposed to be not just a mere step in the entire process of sex but it has its own benefits for the attainment of a successful female orgasm. Here are the various ways in which foreplay helps the female partner achieve a better and stronger orgasm:

Muscle Relaxation

A nice foreplay session's first aim is to relax your body muscles so as to loosen you up for more intense sexual activities. Imagine that you have joined your local gym. On the first day, you reach the arena and start lifting heavy weights thinking it would help you get in fine shape faster. That is a stupid way of going about building a body. Sex is nothing different. Taking it slow and steady is the real key to prepare the female for a nice orgasm. Your muscles work and coordinate with one another better when they are relaxed and loose. Foreplay when executed well, works brilliantly on all the muscles thereby relaxing them enough to prepare for a more intense activity.

Setting of the Mood

If the mood is not set properly, the female partner may not enjoy the entire experience. The right mood goes a long way in establishing trust between partners as it conveys that the male partner knows the exact things that turns on his woman. Foreplay is supposed to be the pre cursor to a good session of sex as it not just readies the body for further activities but also mentally and hormonally prepares you to indulge in what will eventually become an exhausting work.

Stimulates Genitals

A good orgasm is the result of intense lovemaking. However, more than anything it is possible only because the human genitals are fired up enough to perform like rabbits. If the human genitals are not completely excited over the prospect of sex, chances are high that what is going to happen is definitely not going to be satisfying. In order to achieve this very end, t is of prime importance that people indulge in a bit of foreplay before moving on to having hardcore sex.

A limp human penis won't be able to completely satisfy your woman. If you are having a semi erection, do not go ahead and indulge in the sexual activity. Instead give yourself some time and use this to work on some foreplay. A human penis when not fully erect serves little purpose towards the destination of a powerful orgasm. The human vagina is a complex anatomy and requires a fully functional penis to invade it so as to arouse the woman. So if your erection is not full yet, work towards it. Use some oils in the bathroom and exercise a bit before the main act.

Removes Doubts

No relationship is perfect. Couples are always in turmoil over whether they can fully trust each other or not. When foreplay is introduced, it assures the female partner that the male partner is willing to take things slow and not rush into everything. It reaffirms her faith in you and tells her that you are willing to put in the required efforts to win her over steadily and are not planning to user her for sex and then move on to the next girl. This is especially relevant for those couples that have recently come together. The building of trust stage in a relationship is crucial and foreplays instill the much-required faith in the females' minds.

Prevents Anxiety

A lot of people go through self-doubts and low levels of self-confidence right before the first time they indulge in sex. Taking the game to the last level from the very start may not help with such individuals. These individuals are generally in need of morale boosters and faith confirmation. They cannot easily trust a person and are rarely seen showering their affection on any random passerby. When it comes to sex, such people need to be assured over and again that they are not being cheated or duped. They need to be showed that their partners are there to stay. It is helpful for them to know that their partners are trustworthy and they are going to take care of any situations that threatens to arrive during their first sexual encounter. This is specially so with the womenfolk.

From a very tender age they are taught that boys are mean and should not be trusted. Such an influential discouragement from the activity of sex makes them panic even thinking about it. The very beautiful art of sex becomes a taboo for such people and they are not able to imagine themselves indulging in a bit of it. What such a mentality that has been molded from the beginning leads to is Anxiety. Women being tender creatures are more likely to succumb to anxiety attacks than men. When anxiety kicks in during a possible first encounter, it prevents the woman from fully enjoying the activity of sex. If that happens, orgasm becomes a distant dream.

Foreplay is supposed to be that stage of the entire process that is supposed to soothe the nerves of the female partner. It is this step that promises to calm her nerves and assure her that though this is her first time, the male partner knows what he is doing and he is going to take care of any situation that may arise midway.

PREPARE YOURSELF

We shall be discussing the most important element of a good orgasm- you. It all boils down to you when it comes to your female partner achieving a strong orgasm. You are the main player, the showstopper in all of this. If you fail o perform during the hour that is important, everything that you have read and planned so far will go to waste. Hence, it is vital that you work upon you.

Why is working on you important?

Like it has been mentioned above, the most relevant player in the game is you. Whether your female partner receives the best orgasms of her life or not depends entirely upon how you play on your day. However, it is not always that we get what we desire. So it naturally follows that we won't be at the peak of our game every single day of the league. In order to make sure that you are in your form, you need to ensure that you are sexually good most of the days. You should be prepared enough to say randomly yes to a sex session. You may be required to perform in any place at any time. Your female partner deserves a man who is ready all the time. Let us work on it but by bit.

An Appealing Personality

This may not make sense now, as a personality may have very negligible amount of equation with orgasm on the outset. How you look should hardly matter when it comes to how you perform in the bed. However, it is not entirely so. Your personality has got a relevant connection with your orgasmic powers. You, as a man, are supposed to be charismatic, charming and chivalrous all the time. It should be in your very nature that you are strong, well built and powerful not just in terms of body but also with regards to body language.

Women are strange creatures. Trust me on this. Women find the littlest of things to be turning on. It is a man's personality that attracts a woman towards him. Personality works wonders for a man if he knows how to use it. How a man walks, talks, puts forth his points, argues, behaves and converses in the public- everything is put together and the man's sex appeal is accessed. All this happens subconsciously as you are talking to a woman. In the woman's mind she is not just judging you based on how you look, she is also making predictions about your tool size and the shape of your head down there. Like I mentioned before, women are strange creatures. Orgasm for them starts right when they are talking with a man they end up liking or getting drawn towards. Hence, you need to work on your personality to woo women and induce the much-hyped orgasms.

Good Built

Riddle me this- which of the following two stands a better chance of landing a woman at a casual bar? A chiseled hunk in a suit or a pot-bellied man holding a lazy bottle of soda, sitting in a crouched position in the corner? The answer is simple - the former!

Like I said before, for women, orgasms start right when they have a look at a man. This man needs to be not just a good looker but also someone who pays great attention to his physique. A man is nothing without a good body. A well-built physique is not a sign of an alpha male; it is the requirement of any male! A toned body in a man is enough to inspire dirty thoughts in women right when they steal a glance at your muscled you are.

If you are a man with not so great a body, it's time you started hitting the gym daily. Subscribe to your local gym and start working out like crazy. If you seriously want to give your woman the ultimate time of her life, it is vital that you first have one. For that, you have to work on your basic man skills. One of the major ones of them all is a good physique. We are all primal beings. We may have grown all liberal and educated. We claim to find intellectuals hot and sexy however at the end of the day while touching yourself, you always imagine the dumb yet good looking person you always fantasize about.

A lot of what is being propagated regarding intellectualism being the new sexy is a load of fad. We are animals and we have basic animal instincts. We always look for a strong built partner who is expected to survive longer. Darwin was not wrong when he gave his theory of evolution. Every human struggles every day towards just one goal- survival. It is just one part of survival instincts that we look for someone with the right physical features. While men look for curvy and shapely womenfolk, women go after strongly built men who have worked on themselves and developed a body to swoon over. It is only a matter of survival and evolution and there is nothing embarrassing about such desires.

Moreover, besides your body helping you land women, it is also another important and direct factor in your woman enjoying sex to the extent of having good orgasms. A good male body is supposed to do better and more sexual positions than an unhealthy one. A well-built man can lift his woman any way his want and pound her to arouse her to the limit of having an exhausting session of multiple orgasms. When you have strength, you are more open to trying different positions during sex, as you are uninhibited due to your prowess. You are no longer unable to try certain positions because it requires you to apply a lot of strength trying to lift your lady up in a specific position.

A Good Talker

Words have been considered a powerful tool in the history of mankind. Words have been known to wage wars, destroy civilizations and ruin kingdoms. Such is the power of words alone that even strong men have been careful while using it.

Did you know that you could induce orgasm in your woman by simply talking?

Well, newsflash: The Human Tongue can do that in two ways. The real power of words lies in making people do things without having to physically do anything. A modern approach to sex and related activities tells us that it is possible to make your woman cum by simply uttering a few effective words and some gentle and feathery touching. Why do you think great poets in the history of the humankind were good womanizers? They were blessed with the gift of the tongue. They knew the exact words and the proper tone to say them in that had the potential to induce orgasms in their female partners.

The basics of womanizing contain the element of taking. If you are a good talker, you are bound to get successful in almost all aspects of your life. One of these aspects is sex. Researchers have proved that it is indeed possible to bring out the female juices flowing if the man knows the right words and the right way to say them. Here are a few simple techniques to follow if you are looking forward to seduce your woman using words:

First, make a list of all such words that you have noticed to bring an impact in your woman's mood. There are always certain words that women like. Such words could be rough, dirty, arousing or simply ordinary. You do not necessarily have to resort to the dirty talk. Even simple sounding words when given a context have the power to induce orgasmic activity in women. Compile a list of all such words for your woman.

Be minimalistic in your approach. Remember that too many cooks spoil the broth. While using words, never ignore the power of being minimal. The fewer the words, the better their impact. When you end up using too many words that broadens the horizon of your woman's imagination allowing her to mentally envision a range of possibilities. This has an effect of dilution on her imaginations thereby rendering your words redundant, as they don't signify anything particular or singular. However, on the contrary, when you are limited in your word usage, you make sure that the radar of imagination captures exactly what you want her to capture.

In my personal experience, simple words with some history and context work more magic than fluffy and big words that sound and look like they have been picked right from the dictionary. It is in the very nature of ordinary words that they induce really strong emotions in couples when provided a context. There might be words that only you and your partner are privy to.

These words may not even exist in the English dictionary. You may have shared a joke and such words may have lingered on long after this joke has breathed its last. Take help of such words instead of the complicated ones.

Personalize your word usage. If you and your female partner have been a couple for a while, chances are high that you two share a history of conversations that includes the usage of certain words that induce a certain memory or feeling whenever either of you utters them. This is healthy for your relationship. On top of that, these words can be taken help of while trying to induce orgasm in your woman.

Coming right down to business, dirty talk has a magical effect on women. They simply love it when their men hold them from their waists, pull them close for an embrace and whisper dirty and raunchy things in their ears. You can always tell your woman all the things you are going to do to her tonight. Doing so in a public place has an additional character of turning on the women even more. When you express yourself to your woman, you make sure that you make your intentions clear.

A man who uses clear and direct words to tell her woman about the things he is going to do to her in bed scores really good. Women love it when their men invest so much in their sexual performances. When they actively express themselves, it indicates that the men have planned a series of things to do to them tonight. Though you may have just said so for the sake of it, it surely incites them to an extent of getting wet and hence ready for the ultimate orgasm of their lives.

Ways To Make You Last Longer In Bed

So, this is more of a recap with a few new ideas thrown in for good measure. At the end of the day, most men want to be able to last longer in bed, not just those who suffer from premature ejaculation. We all know it isn't any fun for either of you when things end too quickly but, on the other hand, all the media hype that says you should be going at it for half an hour or more is also wrong. Many men are conscious of the fact that they may be finishing just a little too quickly for their partner as all those Hollywood movies and magazines would have you believe women love sessions that go on for hours.

That is all complete and utter rubbish and nothing but hype. That said, there are times when you could do with lasting just a little longer than a few minutes so here are some killer tips to help you hold back for longer:

1.   Back to your teenage years

Remember how, as a teenager, you used to spend what felt like hours kissing and making out without actually having sex? Felt good, didn't it. So, go back to doing that. Spend more time on kissing your partner, on exploring each other using your hands and your mouth before you even think about actually having sex.

2.   Learn how to massage

When you lead a busy life, it becomes quite difficult to find the time for sex and it isn't easy to make the move from your busy working life to a sexy erotic one. Stress is the culprit here and before you can even begin to feel like getting down to it, you need to de-stress. The very best way to do that is through massage, and if you do it properly, both you and your partner will be completely turned on by it. You do need to learn how to do this properly, though; if you don't you can actually cause more problems. Learn to give a very deep and satisfying massage and then each of you takes about 5 or 10 minutes to massage each other before you think about sex. Not only are you really getting in the mood but you will be helping each other to breathe properly and to relax. Foot and back messages are perfect for priming you for pleasure and comfort and, think of it this way – each minute you spend intimately massaging your partner is another minute towards your goal of lasting longer in bed.

3.   Take it in turns

Most sexual sessions are pretty much a give and take pleasure method, in which each of you touches each other at the same time, which means you are both heading for the finish line pretty darn quick. There is a golden rule here if you really want things to take longer – take it in turns to touch each other. From now on, let your partner do the touching while you relax, lie back and take as much pleasure from it as you can without getting too over-excited. Then return the favor; let her lie back while you do the touching and exploring. Both of you need to learn how to use your hands properly to give as much pleasure as possible, leading both of you down the road to arousal but not so quick as it would normally happen.

4.   Control your surroundings

The truth of the matter is when you are in a comfortable position, in comfortable surroundings, a place where either you or your partner is likely to get too over excited, you are more likely to last longer in bed. Don't be tempted with public sex or anything else that could be just that little too exciting for you. If your most comfortable place for sex is in bed then keep it in the bedroom, at least until you have learned how to control your orgasm.

5.   Woman on top

I mentioned this one earlier; by having the woman on top, you don't feel so stimulated. Plus, ask her to take it slowly. Long, hard and fast thrusts are pretty dangerous for a man on the edge! You could also try penetrating her and then not moving for a couple of minutes, just to let yourself get acclimatized to her.

6.   Use the start-stop technique

With this technique, your woman will stimulate you until you start to get close to an orgasm. At this point, tell her that she must stop. When your levels of sexual tension have reduced, it could be as quick as 15 seconds, start again. By doing this frequently, not only will you last longer for that particular session but you will also begin to understand your own feelings and will learn how to stop yourself.

7.   Learn to breathe from the belly

When you breathe deeply, it is actually a direct correlation to ejaculation. So, breathing deeply and slowly should help you to reduce stress and anxiety, thus slowing down your rate of ejaculation. Learn how to breathe so that your belly will rise before your chest does and practice this in conjunction with the start-stop technique. You could also practice the yoga breathing technique I told you about earlier.

8.   Read the Kama Sutra

Preferably together as this will heighten the pleasure for both of you. Plus, you could always try out some of the positions! In all seriousness, though, there is a specific technique that is mentioned that can help you to stay the distance. Using this technique, start off very slowly, with just one in and out stroke per three seconds. Then you can begin to build up the strokes, adding in more, over a session of about four or five minutes until you are at the stage where you are giving one stroke per second. If you feel as if you are about to lose control, stop, stay inside your woman until you regain control and then start from the beginning again

9.   Out of your head

And I do not mean on drugs or alcohol! One of the biggest killers during sex, the one thing that will affect whether you can maintain an erection or not, is stress. And that comes down to what is going through your mind. In the case of premature ejaculation or in those who seem to rush it all the time, the main thoughts are going to be on your abilities and your performance and that will likely push you over the edge. Learn how to change your thinking to positivity and confidence pushing worry and stress out of the way. If you start to feel anxious or stressed during sex, stop, breathe deeply and then focus on your inner self. Get rid of the negative thoughts and put your attention firmly on you and your feelings.

10.   Try new positions

I gave you five positions to try earlier to help you last longer in bed but you could always open that copy of the Kama Sutra. There are specific positions that are designed to make your orgasm happen quicker and others, like the ones I told you about that will prolong things. Experiment, try a few out and see what works and what doesn't.

11.   Learn to control your ejaculatory muscle

When you ejaculate, do you ever wonder what physically causes it to happen? There is a specific muscle that controls your ejaculation and, when it is relaxed, you simply cannot ejaculate, no matter how hard you try. We talked about it earlier – it's called the PC muscle and it what is responsible for letting the semen come out when you come. To control your rate of ejaculation, you have to know how to control this muscle. Practice the exercises we talked about earlier as much as you can until you have almost full control over it. This won't be instant; it can take as much as four weeks to get really good results. It will also take a great deal of regular practice to get it right and become a sexual master.

12.   Learn to control your confidence and mental health

Back in the olden days, it used to be thought that premature ejaculation was the result of mental health problems and men who suffered from it were immediately sent for hypnotherapy or to see a psychiatrist. Obviously neither of those worked very well. While premature ejaculation is a physical condition, it is also linked to mental health and this must not be ignored. You must learn how to manage your concentration levels, your thoughts, and your confidence levels while you are having sex. If you don't, it will have a serious effect on how long you can manage to last for.

13.   Masturbate often

If you truly want to know how to last a long as possible between the sheets, you need to get more in tune with your own sexual responses. To do that, you're going to have to masturbate more. When you begin to stimulate yourself, make sure that you stop before you can't. Let's say that, on a scale of 1 to 10, the orgasm is number 10. So stop yourself at about 8. Make sure you leave time to calm down and then start again, working your way back up that scale. Do this as often as you need to in order to learn how to control yourself.

14.   Learn how to cool down

Whether you suffer from premature ejaculation or not, you should still learn a few methods for cooling down. You can practice these so that, if you do find yourself heading towards being out of control you can stop yourself before you do go over the edge. Do your research and find the methods that will work for you, that will help you to last a bit longer in bed.

15.   Change it up

What is the absolute best thing you can do when you find yourself heading fast toward that point of no return? The biggest piece of advice that I can give you is to change your speed. Men should have a go at teasing their partners; remove your tool from inside her and rub the head up and down over her sex. There are a lot of nerve endings there and this will make her feel great, as well as help to slow you down a bit.

16.   Squeeze

Earlier on, we mentioned the most sensitive parts of the penis. There are three areas that, when squeezed, can help to slow you down and keep you hard. First, when your penis is erect, make a ring with your index finger and your thumb around the base of it and squeeze it. This stimulates a ring around the base of the penis which helps to keep the blood where it should be. The second place is underneath the head of the penis. Applying pressure there can work wonders as it is the hot spot in most men and is full of nerve endings. Lastly, the perineum, the spot that is located in between the anus and the base of your testicles.

All of these techniques are designed for you, with you in mind. Basically, do whatever it takes to make your bedtime sessions last as long as you both want them to.

There is something here that I must reiterate. You may think that it is OK to go for hours in bed and that maybe what you are aiming for. Please don't. Unless your partner is a machine or made of some other substance than blood, skin, and bone, it isn't wise or pleasurable to make sex last for a prolonged period of time, especially not the penetration part of it. It can be painful and uncomfortable, not just for your woman but for you too. Too much thrusting away can cause lubrication to dry up and then it becomes less of the pleasure and much more of the pain. You aren't in the movies and you don't need to perform for the cameras, just for you and her.

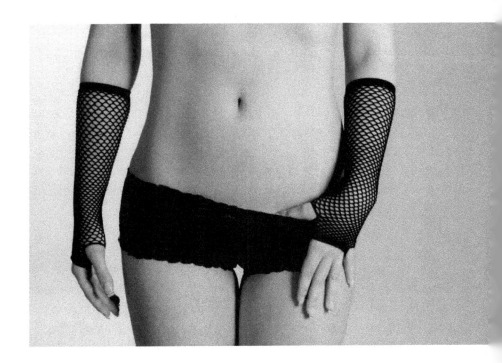

Why There's Need For Sex And The Use Of Different Sex Positions In A Relationship

Sex and sex positions

Sex might mean different things to different people but the bottom line is that it is a very healthy and natural activity that everyone enjoys and find meaningful even with all the different meaning by different people. Sex is not just about vaginal intercourse; sex can be anything that feels sexual which could be vaginal sex, anal sex, hugging, kissing, oral sex or any sexual touching. Sexual activities are very important in a relationship whether one is straight, a lesbian, and bisexual, queer or gay or in any kind of sexual relationship. So basically, sex is any sexual activities that we engage in with our partners for sexual pleasure and gratification. We all know that there will come a time that it might become boring or like a routine if we do not spice things up and this is where sex positions come into play.

Sex positions are the different sultry styles and ways of having orgasmic sex, sex positions should be used just like outfits where different ones should be used at different times. Imagine having sex that makes it looks like you are in your honey moon stage all the time. This is possible if you are acquainted with all the sex positions and its techniques. The fact is that with this, you wouldn't be able to keep your hands away from each other.

·   Tips and tricks to help you love adventurous sex positions

It is one thing is to know about the different hot pleasurable sex positions and orgasmic thrilling styles that can be adopted in the bedroom but the hardest part is being in the mood to explore and to try the suggestions and the new ideas out. The fact is that stepping up and trying something new might be terrifying, scary or uncomfortable for you but there are a lot of ways you can help raise yourself to your sexual height to stop sex drought. If you always need loud moaning, the bed squeaking and having passion sex with your partner then you need to use and love different sex positions. Because it is only this way that you will be able to heighten the fire, the excitement, passion and mind-blowing orgasm that have diminished in your sex life. So to rediscover your lost sexual desires and yearning for having sizzling sex. You can follow the under listed tricks and tips to get yourself to always be in a best mood for new steaming sexual positions.

81

- Get yourself a sexy masseur or masseuse

So you can get yourself in the mood by first wearing a kinky or sexy stuff to be more attractive, and then ask your partner to use hot oils to give you good soothing massages all over the body. This will help to reduce tension and as tension reduces from all part of your muscles, it will put you in a better mood to try your new sultry sex suggestions and positions.

- Keep installing the sex ideas in your mind

You will find yourself horny and needing good sex when you keep seeing an erotic sex picture in advance and how you will be having explosive sex under the sheet when you try out some very kinky sex positions. Make some noises, say sensual things and whisper sweet nothings in your partner ears ahead of time. Just go all naughty with your partner and talk dirty to prepare your mind for some very crazy sex positions that you will be expecting from your partner in the bedroom. All these will add up and make you want to try out hot sex positions and be in love with them.

- Spring up a surprise anywhere

There is something sensual and steamy about having a surprise sex anywhere else in the house especially in the shower and a lot of couples likes sexual encounters in the shower, so you can skip the boring bedroom routine for the time being and try other places and most importantly the shower. Surprise your partner maybe in the shower with erotic kisses, demand some fingering from your partner and totally move your hands all over your partner's body and let your partner's reciprocate same till you get in the mood.

- Flirt and play around with your partner

You can get yourself in the mood for some kinky sex in advance by sending suggestive but subtle text messages to your partner to let him or her know what's on your mind. You can flirt with sending romantic and sex appeal messages to their phone; you can also sound naughty and dirty as possible to give them a clue about your moves. All of these will add to make your sexual advances more persuasive and alluring to your partner and they will respond in a crazy way that will put you in the kind of sex mood you needed.

- Take the initial sex initiative

No need waiting for your partner to be in sexual mood by his or her self, because this route might take longer than you thought. Your partner might not be vocal about it but he or she will definitely appreciate if you take the bold step. You need to supercharge in the bedroom and then create a sexy atmosphere around your partner, he or she would feel aroused and attracted to your body. So go ahead and let them know you are really for sex with them and introduce the sex position you want to try out.

- Introduce porn videos

This could be the key you need to arouse yourself and be in the mood for a new sex position. Porn videos helps to introduce new sizzling sex positions and how to use them, there are a lot of porn videos now you can stream online or download to watch, just get the ones in accordance with your sex fantasies and you can watch it with your partner together. Watching the porn videos together can instantly arouse your partner and you both can practicalize what you are watching or just watched immediately, this will even help to make the experience more adventurous.

- Raise your self confidence

Sometimes you might feel insecure and may have low self esteem and this might lead to you not having physical connection with your partner. You will need to work on this aspect of your sexual life. so you need to remind him constantly that you have a banging body, that your partner will still find your body irresistible and hot, apparently, you need to keep arousing him or her with hot kisses, fondling, cuddling etc. to make them feel desirable by you too. So all these will help you be desirable by partner and your partner will also be irresistible to you too and which will open you up to try out the new sex positions you have in your head.

Outstanding gains of using different sex positions in a relationship

If all you think is a kiss and quickie after a long day of work that will just satisfy your partner, then you are in Lalaland because your partner thinks sex with you is very boring. Your sex life should be explosive that of fun, passion, multiple orgasm and thrills. Your bedmatics skills should be hot and irresistible that your partner will love and be eager to be part of, and as such it always good to spice up your sex life to ignite the gone chemistry or heightened the passion that already exist. So, it is expedient for you and your partner to learn how to unstuck from a sexual routine that must have engulf your sex lives. Give different sex positions a shot to kill boredom that will aid to spark the sexual flames and ignite all the intense feelings for love making. You might not have known but the below points are some killer reasons why you should learn and try out different sex positions in your sex life.

· It will emotionally connect you both

Nothing beats the good old benefits of emotionally connection with a partner after having fantastic bomb sex with one another. You two will stay connected to one another; there will be this subjective feeling that will bond both of you together. This kind of connection will help to arouse strong feelings which will enable you to value mind and soul of your partner and makes you have deep and meaningful conversations with them.

· It will increase intimacy

Introducing new sex positions in the bedroom all the time will keep away unfriendliness and aloofness from partners, so to have a moment of greatest pleasure or rush of sexual excitement with your partner. You must know how to keep things spicy and hot in the bedroom. Good amount of intimacy is needed to keep the connection very strong.

· It offers immense sexual pleasure

Working with some new ideas and sexual suggestions will make you and your partner rediscover your selves, this is like finding the best options that will build on already existing pleasurable zones. By trying new sex position you will discover more pleasurable options you will have to explore and of course the end result is more excitement and enjoyment during sex et al. Again, this will enhance deep penetration for the man and a better thrusting for the woman and these add up to make the sex experience heavenly. This is like finding both G-spot and what can give you both the ultimate satisfaction.

· Easy orgasm for the partners

Nothing is as frustrating as not being able to climax, in fact it shouldn't have a place in your bedroom or a very abnormal thing to experience. I believe orgasm is an experience that no couples want to exclude from their sex session because this is the explosive part of love making and it helps couples to love themselves better after a wow sex session. So using different sex positions in the bedroom can actual help you achieve this explosion effortlessly. It is all about going with the ideal positions and ideas that will give the best result. Of course if one doesn't experiment with the sultry positions learned, it might be counter-productive if one only gets to know about them without exploring and experimenting with them.

· It makes couples to be flexible

Knowing different sex positions and willingly to use them enable you to have several and numerous sex options to explore. Switching things up in the bedroom using the different sexual suggestions provided here will help spice up things in the bedroom. This will help you and your partner stop seeing sex as a routine or chore that needs to be done for the sake of it but what they look forward to having for immense pleasure, getting freaky and exploring another pleasurable zones. Using different sex positions available will make sex for couples or partners be more of a necessity and what should be done to make life more alluring for partners.

Conclusion

Sex is an important part of life and crucial for being in a fulfilling relationship. Whether you have a great sex life and just want to keep experimenting, or you're just starting to explore what makes you and your partner feel good, I hope this guide has been a useful resource for you. By opening up communication with your partner about sex, you can both continue to explore and grow sexually, figuring out how to have the most satisfying sexual relationship possible. Sex is for everyone, from flexible yogis to couch potatoes, so wink at your partner, shimmy out of your clothes, and start having fun!

There is so much to explore, so many parts of our human psyche that are still untapped, waiting for the right key to come unlock them. I believe that almost anyone can be consumed by the allure sex poses. It becomes a challenge to reach certain milestones – losing your virginity, receiving your first oral sex, giving your first oral sex, having sex in public for the first time, trying your first sex toy, making love for the first time. It's fun. There's also a certain amount of ego involved. It feels good to be doing this stuff, and I do think that sex is a fundamental need we have as human beings.

But it's also important not to place too much emphasis on your "success" or "failure" in this conquest. I have been through periods where I was not having any sex, and for whatever reason, I let it affect my self-esteem and my sense of self-worth. This is an unhealthy view of sexuality. You are letting your mind become vulnerable to an outside force that can be largely out of your control. The conquest should not be a conquest at all. There should not be anything to conquer, or to do better than someone else, or to do before someone else.

It should be an exploration of this aspect of life. You should try your best to seek the truth in your sex life. Find out what you truly want. Find a partner or partners who share your desires. Make the most of those experiences. Don't do this for personal gain or to make yourself feel better. Don't do it to selfishly "get yourself off."

Do it to genuinely share a unique connection with someone.

Do it to have the most fun you possibly can.

I mean, that's what this is all about right? Having a good time?

So, take what you have learned here, go forth in your sex life with confidence and determination to find that truth which only you can find.

SEX POSITIONS

Introduction

The birds and the bees talk probably made us uncomfortable the first time we had it. It felt awkward, embarrassing, and we were probably red in the face throughout the entire thing. Fast forward to adulthood, and it seems we still haven't quite mastered what it takes to experience the kind of mind-blowing sex that seems to rock our world. Men, it would seem, can do it at any time with a snap of the finger. Women, however, need the mood set right, scented candles, to feel in the mood before anything can get going. Well, that's the stereotype anyway. But how much truth is there to these perpetuated stereotypes? Do men have stronger sex drives? What about women? What does sex mean for them? For that matter, what do men and women in all honestly want to achieve out of their sexual experience?

Let's get the ball rolling with a couple of quick facts. Firstly, yes, as it turns out, numerous studies have shown that men have much higher sex drives compared to women. The source of a woman's libido, on the other hand, is much harder to pinpoint. The consensus is that women attach a more emotional value to the act of sex, but it turns out social and cultural factors now influence their opinions on sex too. Lead author of a major sexual practices survey (The Social Organization of Sexuality: Sexual Practices in the United States), Edward O. Laumann, Ph.D., states that a woman's sexual desire is sensitive to her context and environment. Laumann and other researchers have identified several patterns in the sex drives of men and women (although these patterns may vary depending on the individual and the context):

• The Road to Satisfaction Is More Complicated for Women – Many women have a romanticized notion of sex. Like a plot straight out of a romance novel, sex needs to be more subjective and contextual, a longing that fuels their sexual desire. By contrast, men don't need such a vivid imagination to get them going. A lot of men see sex as the way they connect with their partners, whereas women need to get to know their partners first, talk, connect, and then hop into bed.

• Men Think About Sex More Than Women – Laumann claims that most adult men below 60 thinks about it at least once a day on average. In contrast, only a quarter of women think about it as often. Both men and women fantasize about sex much less as they grow older, but men still fantasize about it more.

• Getting A Woman Aroused Is More Complicated – Some women even have a hard time explaining what turns them on. In a sexual study done by researcher Meredith Chivers (Northwestern University) and her colleagues, a group of men and women (both heterosexual and homosexual) were shown erotic films and asked to describe their level of arousal. Devices were attached to their genitals to measure their actual levels of sexual arousal, and the results were not surprising. Men (heterosexual) were aroused by male-female and female-female sex. Homosexual men were aroused by male-male sex, and in both cases, the measuring devices on their genitals backed up those findings. Heterosexual women were more aroused by male-female depictions of sex, but the measuring devices on their genitals showed they responded to all forms of sexual depictions.

• Men Want It More Often – At the beginning of a relationship, during and several years after, a man is likely to seek out sex more avidly than a woman will. Laumann states that two-thirds of men masturbate, and only about 40% of women do it. Over their lifetime, men are more likely to have more sexual partners than women do.

• Women Are Influenced Culturally and Socially – As it turns out, women are influenced more than men by their immediate environment. Their sexual practices, desires, and attitudes are likely to change with time compared to men. The attitudes that their peers have about sex are also likely to influence them to a certain degree.

Sex and The Truth About How Women Feel

For a lot of women, sex is a deep and meaningful way of connecting with their partners, especially if they love them. A man's orgasm may happen a lot quicker, but when a woman orgasms, it is incredibly powerful. Her capacity for pleasure even leads to the possibility of multiple orgasms when done with the right partner. Men and women are different from each other in so many ways, and when it comes to sex, here's the truth about how women feel and what makes their take on sex different from their male counterparts:

• It's A Mind, Not A Body Thing – Women's bodies are different hormonally, and that's one of the reasons why they don't crave sex in the same physical manner men do. Testosterone is present in both genders and is the hormone responsible for triggering this sexual desire but to varying degrees. In men, the hormone is practically screaming out loud to have sex. In women, that hormone is sometimes nothing more than a whisper. For many women, sex begins in mind with a lot of imagination and fantasy, sometimes even picturing what it would be like with her partner to get her juices flowing.

• Women Want to Be Desired – Canadian researcher and sexologist Meredith Chivers claims for women, "to be desired is the orgasm." Sure, an attractive man might make her feel hot under the collar for him, but when she imagines what he thinks about her, that's when it hits home. Knowing a man finds her desirable ignites her arousal.

• Other Factors Influence Desire – Women do love sex, but there are a lot of factors these days that might affect their level of desire. Feeling tired after a long day at the office or taking care of the kids. Physiological problems, feeling emotional, even menopause might impact her desire to get intimate with her partner. Having other things on their mind like getting the laundry done, running through the list of chores in their mind, being distracted by work, friends, or family could put the brakes on her desire.

• It's Contextual – The ups and downs of being in a relationship could cause some women to disengage from sex out of their desire to protect themselves. Women need to feel safe emotionally, and she needs to know that she is in a safe enough place with her partner, where she can be free to open her heart to him. Sex is one way a woman expresses her love for her partner. Being motivated by love could sometimes lead her to give her partner sex, even though she may not have any real desire for it at that moment. She's doing it because she knows that her partner wants it.

• Love and Sex Is Part of A Package – Spending time together, staying up all night talking, working together as a couple, feel loved and appreciated, celebrating, going on holidays together, giving each other gives, being affectionate, love. All these things are part of a packaged deal for a lot of women, and sex is part of that package. It's not as easy for a lot of women to have sex with no strings attached and achieve the kind of mind-blowing, earthshaking sex that both men and women crave deep down.

Sex and The Truth About How Men Feel

As for men, their perspective on sex is entirely different from their female counterparts. Of course, this is going to differ based on the individual (just as how the examples above would differ depending on the woman), but some common themes about what men feel when it comes to sex include:

• It Starts Physically – Men are less likely to be prompted by the emotional connection for sex the way women are. Men are driven by the high levels of testosterone in their bodies, and many can have an erection at the slightest trigger, especially in younger men. For the average adult male, the mere sight of his partner stepping out of the bathroom fresh from a shower is enough to cause a reason in his body. Sex is very much a physical thing for men.

• It Energizes Them – The energy is derived from all those hormones coursing through his veins. The hormones a man experiences with sex energizes him in the same way he is driven to pursue his passion, his purpose, his career, even pursue a partner he is interested in. Sex is an exciting and thrilling prospect for the average healthy male, and his body welcomes any opportunity to receive such pleasure. It doesn't take much to get him excited, either. A smile, being flirtatious, sexual innuendos, the curves of the woman's body underneath her clothes is enough to send his excitement skyrocketing.

• Men Are Hungry for It – Quite literally. Their bodies crave for sex in the same way one might crave for food. Given that men think about sex a lot more than women do, it is easy to see why any opportunity to satisfy that hunger is going to be met with delight.

• Men Give Love Through Sex Too – It's not always a wham, bam, thank you ma'am approach with men. They make not be as emotionally obvious as women are, but sex is a way many men express their love and appreciation for their partners too. Men want to know they please their partners, and he welcomes the chance to be a better lover to his partner. The sexual release that a man experiences with the woman he loves is an

94

exquisite pleasure. They may not express it the same way, but they feel a deep sense of connection and attachment to their partners too.

Sexual Positions

If you are a novice when it comes to sex, the act can seem really intimidating and overwhelming. When you enter into a sexual relationship, it takes time for you to learn what you like, what your partner likes, and what balance strikes the best chord with you both. Getting tense and worrying about the situation only makes it worse, so my first piece of advice is to take a deep breath and allow yourself to relax. Allow things to move at a natural pace and do not try to rush. Start off with simple positions that are not too challenging so that you can focus on the feelings they arouse. This will allow you to feel connected and safe with your partner. Here are a few simple sex positions that every beginner should try.

You may not have tried tantric sex, but perhaps it's time you did. The idea of Tantric sex goes back generations and the Kama Sutra explained all about it. This was a book written by a priest and the intention of the book was to allow couples to find perfect harmony in their marriages, so that the love lasted longer and the couple found close bonding within their relationship. The same applies today and you can experiment with different lovemaking techniques that enhance your love life. She will love you for it because all of these practices are caring and that's the nature of a woman.

When you decide to try Tantric sex, you will need to have warmed coconut oil for massage that leads to lovemaking. You will also need to prepare the bedroom so that it is a temple of pleasure. Make sure that you protect your sheets with large towels and that you have both discoursed tantric sex in advance. Choose an evening when you have lots of time on your hands and you know you won't be interrupted.

Massage plays a large role in the kind of sexual activity you share with your partner. It's all about satisfying your partner, rather than yourself. Massaging her clitoris isn't all there is to it. Massage inside her and find her G spot. Massage the area of the anus as well if you have both consented to it. You will find that this area actually links with her G spot internally and that you are likely to get a very marked response to this massage. Similarly, she can massage you and the most sensitive area she can massage is the area between the testicles and the back passage because it is here that all of your sexual senses are awakened.

Positions suitable to tantric sex

Closeness and intimacy is everything when you are making love in the tantric way. You may decide that you want to pleasure her in a gentle way and letting her sit on your lap and then sitting up to join her is a good way to start making love. Your bodies will slide together and she will be able to hold onto you or lean back so that you can play with her clitoris as well as entering her vagina. Again, slow rocking will help you to excite each other and you need to learn to hold off on climaxing. When you feel she is near climax, stop. Then start all over again. The idea of tantric sex is to make the climax something explosive and the more you hold off on climaxing the huger the climax will become. Make sure that you are both on the same page. You can read the Kama Sutra together and try many of the intimate positions suggested, making sure that the climax isn't the whole focus of lovemaking. The focus is on improving the pleasure for your partner and extending that pleasure.

The Bow – This position is a very powerful position and allows full penetration. It also allows a man maximum thrust while a woman's hands can be used to massage the testicles. The woman lies on her back and places her feet onto the chest of her man who is kneeling between her legs. Her behind is raised and you may find it more comfortable if you use a cushion so that the level is perfect for entry into her. Before entering her, make sure that she is massaged and that the oils allow easy penetration. Get her to push against your chest with her feet because this gives you more thrust and more control over the lovemaking process. While you are making love in this way, she can massage you and this helps to make your orgasm even stronger.

Crossed leg lovemaking – This may sound like a contradiction in terms, but it is the position that derives this title because of the stance taken. A man lays his woman onto a table edge. Her legs are lifted to his shoulders but before placing them onto his shoulders, he crosses her legs. You may wonder why the crossing of the legs is so essential but this is because of the woman's anatomy. It gives her greater control over the muscles within the vagina and she is able to move her body in rhythm with his so that she gains maximum thrust and he gains maximum friction. It's a wonderful way to make love and something that will make both the man and the woman very happy indeed.

If you introduce tantric sexual practices into your lovemaking, you will find that you will be less shy of each other and will be able to share a lot more of your desires with your partner as well as being open to listen to hers. She may have a wealth of ideas that will spice up your love life, but she needs to have total trust in your reactions. Be open and talk to her. Let her know that the rules of the bedroom are that she can feel free to talk about her own sexual desires as well as fulfilling yours. Many women are a little shy about talking about sex, so will need that level of reassurance that helps them to open up and be honest. It isn't lack of honesty. It's being afraid of your reactions that make a woman hold back from being adventurous. Show her that you want her to be happy in bed and listen to what she says. She may have ideas that will fill your lovemaking with a new sense of happiness and contentment.

If you are a novice when it comes to sex, the act can seem really intimidating and overwhelming. When you enter into a sexual relationship, it takes time for you to learn what you like, what your partner likes, and what balance strikes the best chord with you both. Getting tense and worrying about the situation only makes it worse, so my first piece of advice is to take a deep breath and allow yourself to relax. Allow things to move at a natural pace and do not try to rush. Start off with simple positions that are not too challenging so that you can focus on the feelings they arouse. This will allow you to feel connected and safe with your partner. Here are a few simple sex positions that every beginner should try.

Missionary Position

This position is famous for its simplicity and the great variation that it allows for both partners. By simply changing the angle of your legs, you can change the sensations aroused from this position. It allows for a deep feeling of connection between partners while allowing deep penetration. It is also one of the most common positions that allow women to orgasm from penetrative sex. This is due to the fact that the man's penis is more likely to hit the woman's g-spot with inward strokes of his penis. To get started with the basic missionary position, the woman lies on her back and the man gets into position between her spread thighs so that their pubic regions are aligned and penetration is possible.

Lying Face to Face

This position is great for beginners as it allows you to both be comfortable and be in tune with each other's needs because of the intimacy it creates due to the eye contact and deep penetration. To do this position, all you have to do is lie on your sides facing each other. The woman should lie slightly higher than the man with her hips above his. She should then place her top leg over his hips and allow his penis to slide inside of her.

Spooning

This position is great for G-spot stimulation and allows for lots of skin-to-skin contact. It is like cuddling and sex in one. The man can easily reach around and stimulate the woman's clit in this position. This is a simple position for couples to achieve. Lay in a spooning position with the woman's hips slightly above the man's. Her top leg should be slightly lifted so that he can penetrate her.

Woman on Top

In this position, the woman straddles the man while he sits so that their faces are close together. This position allows the woman more control but still allows the couple to be connected emotionally. To get in this position, the man must be seated and reclined against something like a couch or a wall. The woman straddles him until their genitals are aligned and penetration is possible.

Doggy Style

This position is great for deeper penetration and leaves both the man's and woman's hands-free for clitoral play and stimulation. To get into this position, the woman rests on her hands and knees with her legs spread so that her partner can get behind her. She can adjust the width of her legs closer or wider to accommodate height differences and to allow for the variations in penetration.

Experimental Sexual Positions for Beginners

Variety is the spice of life, and this is also true for sex. Doing the same positions over and over again can quickly become boring and make a couple's sex life become stagnant. This does not have to happen to you and your partner. Even if you are both beginners to sex, you can switch things up and keep things spicy with the position outlined below.

Missionary Position Variations

Remember that I said that the missionary position allows for great versatility. By lifting the woman's feet off the bed and pushing her knees closer to her chest, this variation in the missionary position allows for deeper penetration and greater access to the G-spot. If the woman is particularly limber, she can place her ankles on the man's shoulders for an even greater lift of her buttocks off the surface that they are lying on.

You can also alter the missionary position by placing a pillow underneath the woman's hips. This missionary variation allows the man's body to rub against the woman's clitoris with every inward stroke of his penis. This makes the woman more likely to orgasm from the position.

In the missionary position, you can also experiment with the woman lifting one leg at a time and having the man lift his chest at different angles away from her body. Small things can make a huge difference, and the variations that you can add to the missionary position are a testament to that fact.

Modified Doggy Style

This position is great for participating in dirty talk as the man's mouth is close to the woman's ear. In this position, the woman lies on her stomach with her hips tilted towards the man who lies behind her. A pillow under the woman's hips can allow the couple to find the right angle for pleasurable penetration. In addition, this is a great position for a woman who would like to show off her derriere to her partner if it is a feature that she is proud of.

Dangling Over the Bed

This position is easy on a man's body as it does not require him to hold his body up with his arms. Since the woman is lying on the edge of a bed with her legs hanging off, he simply has to place himself between her thighs, penetrate her, and thrust them both to a happy finish.

Sex Positions to Help You Get Over Insecurities

Having body issues and feeling insecure about your body is not something that is new, and both men and women suffer from the condition that can sometimes be debilitating. These insecurities can, of course, transfer into your sex life as you need to bare your body to have good sex. The great thing about having a supportive sex partner is that they can help you get over these insecurities and perceived flaws since most of the time we are a lot harder on ourselves and see flaws that other people do not.

Of course, you can help get over these insecurities by addressing them in individual ways such as going to the gym and dieting if you feel that you are overweight. In the bedroom, to help get over your insecurities, a great technique is to find the positions that highlight the features you find most attractive about yourself.

Before we look at some of the sex positions that will allow you to feel less insecure about your body, there are a few other things that you can do to boost your self-confidence in your physical appearance:

• Learn to love yourself and build your self-esteem. No matter the sexual positions that you try, if, at the end of the day, you do not love yourself for who you are and what you look like, your insecurities will always rear their head.

• Spend more time naked. Get familiar with what it feels like to be naked and become intimate with your own body so that when it comes time to be sexually intimate with your partner, you are less likely to be uncomfortable in your own skin.

• Disassociate with people who speak negatively to you about you. Associating with toxic people who not only talk negatively about your body but about their own has a negative impact on you. Therefore, if you have people like this in your life, it is time to have a frank and open discussion about how their words affect you, and if they are not willing to change, then you need to think about cutting them out of your life.

Without further ado, here are a few sexual positions that will encourage you to have a better body image about yourself:

101

Cowgirl

This position is great for helping you get over insecurities because it brings any issues that may be had to the forefront so that they can be dealt with. For example, if a woman is insecure about her breasts, in this position her partner has a full view of them and can reassure her of her beauty and uniqueness. This is also a great position for a woman who feels that her breasts are one of her best assets and wants to show them off to her partner.

This position is great for beginners because it provides body views and great eye contact. To get into this position, the woman straddles her partner and guides his penis to penetrate her. She should use her hands and knees for balance. She bounces her hips up and down to provide stimulation to both herself and her partner. The man can aid this by lifting his hips up and down as well and supporting her with his arms. In this position, the woman can control the speed and intensity of the strokes. She can also widen her knees or bring them closer to change the depth of penetration.

The Three-Legged Dog Position

This position is great for the promotion of dirty talk and having eye contact in addition to having full upper body contact. It allows both partners to concentrate on their emotional connection rather than physical appearances. Therefore, it is great for people with insecurities since the emphasis is placed on eye contact rather than on each other's bodies. This position involves both parties standing. To aid with equilibrium, one party can lean against a wall. The woman leans into the man with her legs separated and hikes one leg over his hips so that he can penetrate her.

In a Chair

This position is great for reassuring insecurities for the same reasons that the above position is. It allows for lots of upper body contact and lots of eye contact. In this position, the man sits in a chair and the woman straddles him with her thighs on either side of his body. She can bounce up and down or grind against him to stimulate them both.

Lotus

In this position, the man sits crossed-legged on a flat, comfortable surface, and the woman sits on his lap so that they are facing each other. She wraps her legs and arms around him. They can both aid in the penetration and stimulation of each other. This position helps both parties feel secure in the fact that they are emotionally connected with eye contact. Just like the spooning position, this is sex and cuddling in one, and all the associated feel-good hormones are released when couples engage in sex in this position.

Illustrations of Sexual Positions
Missionary 180

Pressed Missionary

Being an enthusiastic sex position among the family of missionary sex position, it is quite amazing and marvelous. The woman lies straight with her back on the ground and legs bent on the knees, heading back towards her abdomen, providing full exposure of her holes to her partner. On the other hand, the man lies on top of her body, with face right in front of her face, providing enthusiastic kissing and licking experiences for both partners. The man caresses her hair or shoulders with his hands while the woman pushes him towards herself to ensure reddish physical contact. Being exposed in this position, woman allows her partner to go deep inside her vagina or anal hole, providing mild sex experience and unforgettable moments for both. This position allows the man to go harder on his female partner by strongly aiming and pushing to go deep inside the depths of the vagina or anal hole. Anal inclusion could be more interesting for the couple as it offers more pleasures through anal gaping.

Crabby Groundhog

Another enthusiastic sex position from the family of man on top sex positions is crabby groundhog. It entails the woman lying straight on her abdomen and upper body lifted by bending elbows. The man sits on her pelvis, reclining backward into a crab position. This position seems a bit difficult for men who find it to be straining. This straining causes you to pain in the lower back. These drawbacks can be reduced by placing a few pillows under the women's pelvis and making the angle of penetration more horizontal. This horizontal angle might become easier to go for strong stimulation, strong bumping, and a bit shallow penetration. This position allows clitoral stimulation due to the rubbing of the penis with vaginal lips. Thus, makes it an amazing and mild experience for both partners. Going into anus hole of your partner could be difficult because of tilted angle and less availability. If you wanna try some tricky sex with an adventurous ride, you must try this with your partner.

Pressed Wrapped Bull

If you wanna try an adventurous delight applauded with sensational kissing, licking and physical stimulated response, then you must try pressed wrapped bull once. It requires you and your lady to be stretchy enough to perform it in the best way, but it's worth it. It has the power to steer the partners towards their self. The woman lies on the ground with her back and her pelvis is lifted by the man in order to place it in his lap. Her legs are bent on her knees, heading backward. While the man sits on the ground with his legs driven apart to accommodate her body between his legs. He is reclined forward on his woman to suck her boobs, lick her body and kiss her gently to spice up the sexual intercourse. Sex with these prerequisites becomes delightful and habitual. This position allows the man to go inside the vagina and anal hole up to his choice or according to his lady's will. Meanwhile, she can feel every inch of the penis, shattering her holes to go deep inside and make a pleasurable passageway. Squeezing her boobs while penetrating her as fast as you can add enough excitement to transform you both into wild beasts.

Planted Wrapped Bull

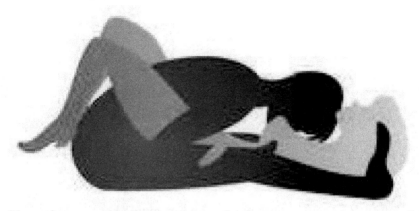

Planted wrapped bull is another enthusiastic sex experience out of the class of man on top and bull variations. This is quite fantastic due to its approach and delightful experience. In this position, the woman lies on the ground with her back and her pelvis aligned with her partner's penis. Her legs are bent and lifted above the ground by her man who uses his hands to push her towards himself to ensure deeper penetration and stronger stimulations. The man sits on the ground with straight legs driven apart to accommodate her body and leaned forward to kiss her boobs, abdomen, shoulders, and lips. He can thoroughly lick her body to replenish the sexual intercourse and turn sex into a mild experience. With every strong bump, his penis visits the depths of the vagina or anal hole and fills him with filthy affection. The more hard he goes, the more plausible it will be to have sex with full intent.

Sex Positions for Advanced

Woman on Top

Lying Rodeo

Anastasiia Frizen - © 123RF.com

A profound sex position with women on top, giving her the dominance and respect over her male partner is famously known as lying rodeo. This shows extremism to leaning forward, as the woman lies on her abdomen on the legs of her man, with her pelvis right above the penis of the man, who is lying straight on the ground, and allowing easy vaginal intercourse. If you love to give foot job, then this position is made absolutely for you. More attention and consideration should be required for the penile angle as penetration wouldn't be straight forward. For men, this position could be a little difficult as it is slow to the start but offers many enthusiastic dealings and full exposure of her holes. The men can see every inch of his penis going inside her holes. This might be a little tricky for men but amazing for women who can control the penis inclusion as well as the bumping speed.

Arched Cowgirl

Anastasiia Frizen - © 123RF.com

This is quite an amazing yet classical position as it belongs to the most favorite cowgirl sex positions family. In this position, the man lies on his back with straight legs. While the women, being on top, kneels over him, arched backward and sustains herself with hands on the floor. This position allows the women to move and haul according to her choice and will. Therefore, the majority of the movement in this position comes from the women lifting, rocking, bumping hardly and rotating her hips. The man puts his hands on her thighs and caresses her legs to stimulate her joys and plausible pleasures. The second variation is playing with her breasts, which will not only stimulate her sex experience to mildness but also indulge both thoroughly in sex. This position also offers a treat of sight-seeing of penis inclusion to her holes. Frictionless inclusions with both vaginal and anal intercourse are guaranteed to delight both partners. The more intense you are to try this position, the more joyous it will be for you and your partner. Being an advanced yet easy sex position, this can be easily performed every time you like.

Planted Arched Cowgirl

Anastasiia Frizen - © 123RF.com

Yet another enthusiastic treat from the family of cowgirl and woman on top is planted arched cowgirl. This position is an extension of the arched cowgirl. It involves the man, lying on the ground with the upper body lifted, that sustains himself with fists on the floor. While the woman, being on top, sits on his abdomen, arched backward just like in the arched cowgirl position. This position allows the man to not only explore the sight-seeing of penis inclusion but also delights him with clitoral playing and stimulate her nerves to go wild towards the sexual approach. On the other hand, the woman opens her legs wide apart to give him full access, together with deeper penetration and frictionless inclusion. Woman, being on top, is captivated with controls over penetration and movements according to her choice. The movements mostly come from her side when she lifts, rocks and rotates her hips. Both partners, in this position, can catch each other's emotions and move in a rhythm that will bring more satisfaction for both of them.

Bridged Cowgirl

Anastasiia Frizen - © 123RF.com

One of the adventurous and enthusiastic positions from the cowgirl family is bridged cowgirl. This is unique according to its approach and sex experience. It involves the man settling down with bouncy abdomen, lifting while touching the ground with hands. On the other hand, the woman, being on top, sits on his abdomen, facing towards his head and praising him with her weight. This position allows deeper penetration and strong stimulation together with frictionless inclusion. It goes really hard for the male partner as he is not able to see going through and feel much difficulty in maintaining this position while lifting the weight of his women too. On the other hand, women can also not freely bounce on the penis because of her feet not touching the ground and letting her balance her body by herself. This position offers less intensity with less movement and hence, lesser satisfaction and joys.

Facedown Cowgirl

Yet another furious and adventurous sex position from the family of cowgirl and woman on top sex positions is facedown cowgirl. This position entails the man lying straight, with straight legs on the bed and upper body inclined downward with shoulders touching the ground and supporting his body. On the other hand, the woman sits on his penis at the cutting edge of the bed and balances her body being arched backward and hands-on bed to support her body leaning backward. This position offers complete control and movements assigned to the woman. She can control the penetration angle as well as the penetration length. The more she settles her down, the more penis length will be included in both of the holes. The man can caress her legs and play with her clit to spice up the sex experience, even if can't play with her boobs. Playing with her clit could bring more joys for both of them that will indulge them deeply and forever.

Sex Positions for Advanced

from Behind

Planted Sinner

Anastasiia Frizen - © 123RF.com

An amazing position belonging to the family of sex from behind is planted sinner. In this variation of sex, the man lies straight on the floor with legs fully straighten; whereas, the woman is lying on his body facing away from his face to give behind ways sex, while her legs are planted closer to the action. Man sustains the woman by her hips and provides her finer control over her pelvis that lies above the penis. He can go through the anal hole with heavy frictions and therefore guarantee anal gaping. While for vaginal intercourse, this seems a bit difficult as vagina lies a bit above and therefore it guarantees strong stimulation and rubbing with the inner lips of the vagina. This position allows less deep penetration with strong rubbing and enthusiastic sexual intensity. Both partners can indulge in sex too hard by going wild in kissing and licking her lips, face and neck. A gentle approach could drive both partners towards the crazy world of extreme sexual intercourse.

Planted Amazon 180

This is another amazing sex position belonging to the family of sex from behind and quite similar to amazon 180 variation. Is also known as the backpack sex position. It involves the woman on her feet, facing away

Anastasiia Frizen - © 123RF.com

from the man, giving him full penile exposure to her holes and allowing him to go in the hole of his choice. She opens her legs to give room to her partner and, on the other hand, the man places his feet on her back to sustain her at the right spot. The best thing about this position is that she sits on his penis allowing him to go deep and feel every inch of vaginal depth and anal gaping together with full back exposure and pleasurable sight-seeing of the penis going deep inside the holes. While for woman, as she is sitting on the penis, she can decide how much length of the penis to digest and in which hole, making this position perfect for women that like to have control. Sensible and enthusiastic sex with mildness and furiousness is guaranteed in this sex position to delight both partners with satisfaction.

Folded Amazon 180

Anastasiia Frizen - © 123RF.com

This is another variation from the family of amazon sex positions and sex from behind family and is commonly known as folded amazon 180. This involves the woman sitting on his lap to allow thorough access of the penis for both the vagina and anal hole. She sits with kneeling legs while the man lies straight on the ground with kneeling legs and hands on her ass to sustain her body. On the other hand, the woman places her hands on his knees to support her body. As the woman sits on his penis, this position guarantees strong stimulation with extravagant penile attributions and deeper penetrations. However, the woman can control the length of the penis going inside by lifting her ass up. She can spice up her feelings and sensuality by going hard with rocking, lifting and tilting her ass sideways to allow fractioned stimulation and extreme sex experience together with mildness and extreme sexual intent.

Fire Hydrant

Plausible and amazing sex experience is guaranteed in fire hydrant sex position. A marvelous experience is guaranteed with the woman lifting her one leg straight up and out sideways. While the other leg is used to sustain herself on the elbow. The man stands on his knees right behind her pelvis to aim straight at the vagina and supports her straighten leg by his hand while the other hand is placed on her ass to caress her body. This position allows strong bumping and stimulation together with harsh going and deeper penetrations as no friction and hurdles come in the way to the vagina. The harsher you aim at the vagina, the deeper it will be included inside and up to every inch of the penis. The woman feels the intent and loves to enjoy the fuller length of the penis shattering her hole and deeply delighting her sex experience. This is quite a marvelous sex position if tried with a pillow right beneath her folded knee. It requires a little bit of stamina by the woman side to be performed, but it offers enormous rewards.

Supported Aerial Doggy

Anastasiia Frizen - © 123RF.com

A pretty amazing and marvelous sex position, belonging to the group of sex from behind, is supported aerial doggy sex. This position seems a bit difficult for men having a thin body figure and leaned muscles. This is a versatile sex position and favored by many. The man's body is lifted and sustains himself by his hands placed on the bed, with legs straight backward lying in the air. Advanced level sex freaks more often to visit this enthusiastic sexual intercourse as it involves mildness and craziness. The woman would feel a lot more comfortable in this sex position when thrusting harder and with stronger intent to go deep inside the vaginal hole. Going with anal gaping could be a feast for joy and enjoyment as the anal hole is nearer and could be shattered with less power. The harsher you go on with bumping to your lady, the more sensible it will be.

Standing Squatting Rodeo

Anastasiia Frizen - © 123RF.com

Another amazing position from the family of sex from behind is standing
squatting rodeo. This involves the woman sitting on the man's penis with legs
folded and leaned on the bench or bed where they are experiencing sexual
intercourse. Moreover, the woman sustains herself on feet, that are placed
near the body on the bench or bed. On the other hand, the man lies straight
on the bench with legs folded on the knees and rested feet on the ground.
The more intense you aim at the vagina, the deeper it will be, but it requires
the placement of the vaginal hole right above the penis to guarantee
frictionless and deeper penetration. If you go soft with tilted angles or
different angles expect right above the penis, the inclusion will not be great,
as it will bend the penis and due to the resting of woman's ass on the penis
of the man. This position is quite amazing, sensible, enthusiastic and fantastic
for every frequent sex freak to indulge deep and turn your partner towards
yourself with a little effort to reward you more.

Tantra

Before beginning with tantric sex, it is pivotal to comprehend the idea of Tantra. The act of Tantra can be followed back to antiquated India, where a few holy people and blessed men used to take part in different ceremonial and meditational systems. This system is accepted to have been in presence since the fifth century A.D., and it was seen as a technique that would enable an individual saddle to divine cognizance just as their still, small voice. This idea traversed the globe and brought about the cutting-edge use of the term Tantra accepting another importance through and through. The term Tantra is prominently connected with the act of Tantric sex. This includes participating in a sexual demonstration with the purpose of collecting divine cognizance together. To lay it out plainly, tantric sex is a training that is used for arriving at sexual nirvana.

History of Tantra

There is some indefinite quality with respect to the birthplace of the idea of tantric sex, however it is a prevalent view that a network, alluded to as the "Lemurian" individuals were viewed as the primary individuals to rehearse this specific type of holy sex. They thought about the human body as an awesome vessel and used different animating procedures for connecting with the senses so as to bring in spiritual liberation. A few people will, in general, accept that Tantra is identified with the old Indian act of "yoga" too, since these two systems use distinctive substantial stances for shaping a bond with the Cosmos.

Tantric sex has increased a great deal of prevalence in the ongoing past and it has gotten well known in the western world with a ton of famous people like Sting, Madonna and even the late Steve Jobs who had confessed to having attempted this system. Presently, it has gradually discovered acknowledgment everywhere throughout the world. A few idealists do have faith in its viability in accomplishing more noteworthy delight.

Tantric sex fulfills individuals genuinely, intellectually and deeply too. Tantric sex gives total fulfillment and causes the whole body to feel incredibly pleasurable, helps in sincerely interfacing with one's partner and on a deep level; it helps in the amalgamation of two spirits and carries them closer to godliness.

Tantra uses two energies; the female and the male energies. The female energy is alluded to as Shakti, and the male energy is known as Shiva. Shakti and Shiva are Hindu divine beings, and their object of worship revere includes the venerating of Ling and Yon. Linga implies the penis and far off methods the vagina. When a couple participates in tantric sex, then the female energy present in the body, Shakti, ascends through the diverse chakras, and it penetrates through the female community that is alluded to as the Kundalini and afterward it converges with the male energy, alluded to as Shiva. This combination of energies helps in framing a bond that outperforms the human domain.

Different parts of Tantric Sex

There are three significant primary parts of Tantric sex, and these are tantric correspondence, tantric positions and tantric working out. Tantric correspondence is a procedure that helps in the converging of a couple genuinely and intellectually. This aids in bringing them near each other and is fit for transforming a standard couple into perfect partners. Tantric positions are sure places that will help in uniting a couple explicitly. There are distinctive tantric activities just as breathing strategies that will help in harvesting the most out of tantric sex.

Tantric sex helps in liberating the body, brain and soul. This is conceivable through the act of the systems as referenced previously. Quieting one's psyche is a vital part of any training that includes meditation. So also, for practicing tantric sex, it is basic to facilitate your brain. These procedures have been referenced in the book.

In contrast to normal sex, the lessons of tantric sex focus on making the members mindful of their activities while engaged with a sexual demonstration with their partner. If you are aware of your activities, then you can guarantee that you can initiate a sentiment of veneration and even regard for your partner. It is tied in with respecting your body and that of your partner's also. The essential goal of tantric sex is to assist you with loosening up your body and brain. When you can discover this discharge, you will have the option to communicate without any difficulty that will develop and reinforce the security that exists among you and your partner; the sort of love that would bind together your spirits.

Tantric sex encourages your healing

Maybe one of the best potential employments of tantric sex is that it can help in healing your body and soul. It will likewise assist you with letting go of undesirable thoughts and cause your psyche to feel lighter. You may have been harmed before or might have persevered through some type of dismissal in your past connections. Tantric sex will help you in excusing yourself and will assist you with learning to adore yourself by and by and to appreciate your body as you were intended to. Various strategies have been referenced right now will help you in mending and liberating yourself from any blame or injury that you may have persevered. You will see that you will feel progressively engaged if you follow the guidance that has been given right now. Tantric sex will without a doubt, assist you with mending and it is done through the next advances. You should distinguish the occurrence that has harmed you previously. This hurt could have been genuine or nonexistent. In this way, the subsequent stage is to decide if it was genuine or fanciful. Sexual incitement will help you in recognizing the distinction. You will have the option to locate the negative feelings connected to this specific damage and can release them. Replace these negative sentiments with positive feelings and encounters that will enable you to heal.

Tantric sex is in fact enchanted. You will find that the different methods that have been referenced right now not just assist you in relinquishing your feelings of trepidation and hurt, yet they will likewise help you in communicating better. Additionally, as an additional advantage, these strategies will help you in feeling more youthful and increasingly loose.

Myths and Truths

Tantra is tied in with commending sexuality and sexiness. It is a general misinterpretation that Tantra is about sex. Without being completely mindful of the Tantra, individuals have been known to scrutinize it. This area helps in revealing all the fantasies that are related with Tantric sex and Tantra.

Myth #1: Tantric sex is just about sex.

Truth: Tantric sex involves sex, yet it isn't about genital touch. Tantric sex is about the relationship of the spirits and not simply the bodies. Genital touch or sex will just assistance in expanding this relationship between the spirits.

Nonetheless, this is done just when the couple is alright with one another and is prepared for that degree of closeness. Tantric sex includes different perspectives that have literally nothing to do with sex.

Myth #2: If you begin practicing Tantra, then you are just abandoning delight.

Truth: This myth is inexactly founded on the past myth. It is basically a myth. The educating of Tantra do exclude the repudiating of sexual delight, similar to a portion of the yogic practices do. Tantra essentially upgrades the degree of joy that you can understanding. Tantric sex hypothesis doesn't make reference to that you have to deny your wants. Truth be told, Tantric sex energizes the free articulation of your sexual wants. You don't need to imitate a yogi, sit leg over leg or reflect for a long time for shaping a relationship with the Cosmos. Tantra understands the significance of sex in a person's life and it helps in the bridling of the torpid sexual energy present in the body for accomplishing ecstasy. This joy can be accomplished is past anything present in the physical domain.

Myth #3: Tantric sex expands your sexual hunger and the requirement for looking for joy that prompts issues.

Truth: Tantric sex doesn't build your sexual craving or lead you off track as you continued looking for delight. Rather, it will help you in controlling your wants and will likewise help in directing the sexual energy that is available inside your body for a higher reason. You may have not known about your actual potential. Tantric sex doesn't energize participating in sex with various partners. This suspicion has by one way or another advanced into the psyches of numerous and isn't right. As referenced before, Tantric sex will help you in shaping a solid physical and passionate bond with your partner and just develop the deep responsibility that exists between you. Sexuality isn't something that ought to be tossed around carelessly; it should be regarded and valued for accomplishing a more elevated level of cognizance. It isn't tied in with surging towards a climax, however it is tied in with figuring out how to control yourself and your wants. This will help in shaping a more grounded connection towards your partner. You will have the option to shape a relationship that did not depend on physical requirements.

Myth #4: It will transform you into a nymphomaniac.

Truth: Well, this isn't valid, and it is very senseless. Tantric sex helps in discharging all the sexual energy present in the body, and it likewise enables you to communicate as unreservedly as could be allowed, yet this doesn't imply that it will transform you into a nymphomaniac. In any case, there are chances this can be abused. With training, you will have the option to control your wants and quit getting a charge out of unimportant sex.

These normal myths have defaced the picture of Tantric sex in the psyches of the overall population. It Is anything but a forbidden and ought to be drilled uninhibitedly if that is your decision.

The Ten promises of Tantra

When you have decided to follow the lessons of Tantric sex, then there are ten promises that you should recollect. Before beginning, it is significant that you recognize what these vows are. You should feel a feeling of harmony while saying these promises. The ten vows are as per the next:

1.   I vow to find the godliness that exists inside my body.

2.   I vow to regard and seek after the Gods and Goddesses that exist inside my body and that of my partner's also.

3.   I promise to investigate my sexuality as well as my exotic nature too, for ensuring that none of my chakras are being blocked as a result of any feelings.

4.   I vow to find some kind of harmony between my spirit, connections and my environment.

5.   I vow to use this balance for guaranteeing that the remainder of the world finds a sense of contentment too.

6.   I vow to comprehend as well as investigate my erotic nature for guaranteeing that there's congruity in my connections.

7.   I vow to ensure that all the psychological pressure and blockages that exist due to my past or even my present have been evacuated. I will free my soul and communicate with no limitations.

8.   I promise to progress in the direction of reconnecting with my internal identity.

9.   I promise to adore and heal my partner and myself also.

10.   I vow to use the revived sexual energy for making myself progressively sure, delicate and associate with my partner and people around me.

You need to take part and watch

As referenced before, you should ensure that your brain is quiet and calm for practicing tantric sex. This is the main manner by which you will have the option to be a member and an eyewitness also. This implies you should be watching your activities as well as those of your partner too while you are occupied with lovemaking.

When you begin focusing on your activities, then you are an observer. This will help you in relinquishing any tension that you may be encountering. When an individual is having intercourse, paying little heed to their sex, there would be a million meditations and questions experiencing their brains. They would stress over whether they can please their partner. Does their partner like what they are doing? Is it accurate to say that they are doing it right? These inquiries add to the nervousness levels and detract from the capability of unwinding. When you begin the educating of Tantric sex, then you will have the option to observe yourself while occupied with this demonstration. Here are a few systems that will help you in being both a member just as an onlooker.

Mantras

Have you at any point been exhausted to such an extent that you essentially begin murmuring a specific sound ceaselessly? Did this appear to have some sleep-inducing impact on you? Mantras are very like this. They are quiet or even spoken sounds and they evoke a specific response from the body in view of their vibrations. These vibrations compare with all the seven chakras that are available in the body. If you have never encountered this, then have a go at saying "Om" and attract full breaths that would compare with this "Om." You will see that you can quiet yourself down and are additionally

124

ready to center your psyche. You will have the option to control the development of energy that is available inside your body. A mantra has a similar impact at the forefront of your thoughts and your perspective as your preferred music does. You will have the option to quiet yourself down. When you use mantras, your brain can meander any place it satisfies and take you along.

The sounds that you make while saying a mantra are short and redundant in nature. This reiteration causes them to have a sleep-inducing impact. A mantra can be a solitary word, a sentence or even a stanza. If you don't have the foggiest idea about any mantras, then you can make one up all alone. It could even be a sound that you like.

Yantras

A yantra is a numerical system that is frequently used in Tantric sex. You probably won't be partial to arithmetic, yet you ought to know that geometric figures are basic with regards to Tantric sex. You should concentrate on the picture if you need to invigorate your sexuality and an exact figure should be remembered for inspiring a specific response. If you are feeling apprehensive or even restless while participating in sex, you can concentrate on such figures for relinquishing all the negative feelings. Diverse geometric figures are identified with every one of the seven chakras that are available inside the human body. These chakras are the vortices for energy that is put away in the body. One of the celebrated Yantras is the sex point Star of David.

Things that you should reflect Tantric sex

Everybody will have found out about Tantric sex at some point in time, and from different sources. There's a great deal of data accessible about Tantric sex, and this prompts a ton of perplexity. Thusly, it is very normal that you are confounded about what Tantric sex is about. The explanation behind this is very straightforward; how it has been depicted on TV and motion pictures is very unique in relation to what it's really similar to. In this way, it is nothing unexpected that a great many people are misguided about what Tantric sex contains. This, however a shame is related with Tantric sex. It is viewed as an unusual type of sex entertainment or even voodoo! This isn't valid and is unjustifiable. Tantric sex depends on the lessons of Tantra. Tantra is an old fine art that depends on the standards of accomplishing satisfaction and edification, about making every second count and living it with no pointless cultural limitations. Tantric sex is certainly not an insane practice, and it will, actually, assist you with framing an increasingly significant and more grounded bond with your partner. A couple will have the option to encounter sexual closeness more than ever. Right now, will realize what Tantric sex is about.

It's something other than sex

As referenced before, Tantric sex isn't just about sex. This comes as an amazement to many. The physical part of sex incorporates touching, scouring and petting. You will have occupied with this while having ordinary sex. Then what's the distinction between Tantric sex and customary sex? Tantric sex gives equivalent significance to the physical part of sex, yet additionally, the significance of partners being associated on a psychological level as well. It would be very useful if you and your partner could disregard accomplishing a climax and could rather move your concentration towards the demonstration that you are included.

Kamasutra

Kamasutra is an ancient book written in northern India in the language of Sanskrit. It is more than just a book of sex positions, but these days most people only know it for its complex and flexibility-requiring positions for intercourse. The book of Kamasutra includes a general guide to living well in other ways than just through sex. It includes a guide to foreplay, a guide to kissing and touching, other ways to achieve intimacy with your partner such as bathing together, cuddling and giving each other massages. It does also include the sex positions it is known for as well as different types of sex like oral and masturbation. The Kamasutra also touches on same-sex relations, calling this the third nature. It also touches on group relations and a little bit of rough sex.

For a book written so long ago, it is still quite relevant in terms of its discussions on ways to achieve intimacy and how to treat your partner well in a physical sense. You could say that Kamasutra is a guide to love and enjoying a pleasurable life with yourself and also with another person. It can be seen as a guide for a long-term relationship or a marriage to keep sex interesting and to try new forms of intimacy.

The Kamasutra includes 64 sex positions of varying difficulties from a flexibility and strength standpoint. Below we examine some of these positions for you to get a sense of what positions are included in this sacred text of love.

The Milk and Water Embrace

The first Kamasutra position we will look at is The Milk and Water Embrace. This position gets its name from the idea that the two people in this position are enmeshed and become so close that they lose themselves in the other person. Interestingly, this position can be used as a loving embrace after sex, or as a sexual position itself of you add penetration to it.

The man sits on the edge of the bed, his legs planted on the floor. The woman approaches him and climbs into his lap, her face to his. She wraps her legs around his waist and her arms around his neck. He holds onto her by wrapping his arms around her back. From here, she positions herself so that she is open enough to receive his penis, and she can help guide him inside of her. His penis slides into her vagina and to thrust they can work together, with the man using his feet on the floor as support while he moves his hips up and down and the woman can grind her hips on his lap for a pleasurable clit stimulation. If she wants, the woman can touch herself here, or if she wants to remain pressed against her man, she can keep both arms around his neck for a closer embrace.

This position is quite easy to get into, and only requires a bit of strength from the man Both of their bodies are supporting each other in this position which is what makes it so intimate. Their bodies are touching at every point and they can breathe together and feel each other's every heartbeat. This is why this position is said to be two people becoming one, like mixing milk and water, when you can't tell where one ends and the other begins.

The Mare's Position

This position is more dependent on technique than on the position itself, but this could very well change your sexual life forever. In this position, the man sits with his legs stretched out in front of him and his arms back supporting his weight on the bed. The woman straddles him, facing away from him and lowers herself down onto his erect penis. Once inside of her, the woman uses her vaginal muscles to apply and release pressure on the man's penis, almost as if she is milking it. This makes for very pleasurable sensations on both the man's penis and the woman's vagina. This creates more stimulation on the man's penis, and also stronger sensations for the woman's vagina. This also strengthens her vaginal muscles which in time will lead to stronger orgasms for the woman!

The Ascending Position

This position allows the woman to take full control of both her body and the man's penis and is good for women who have some trouble reaching orgasm in other sexual positions. The man takes a passive role in this position, with the woman's weight on top of him which can be a huge turn-on. He can lie back and watch her take control and enjoy the pleasure he is getting from his penis inside of her and from watching the woman gyrate and find pleasure on top of him.

The man lies down on his back on the bed, he can prop up his head on a pillow if he wants a better view of the woman. She sits cross-legged on top of his genital area, her legs crossed over his waistline. She holds onto his penis and puts it into her vagina. She can wait to do this after oral or after giving him a hand job first, or she can get right to the penetration, depending on if they have already done foreplay prior to this. Once he is inside of her, she can lean back and rest her hands on his legs for support if needed. From here, she grinds her hips and can control her hip angles and control the speed of thrusting. In this leaned back position, her clitoris is perfectly accessible to be stimulated with her own hand. The man will be too far to do this for her as he is lying down and her legs are holding his body down. The restriction of his movement by his naked woman will be sure to make the man so horny and frustrated that his penis will be rock hard. She can change the angle of her hips to reach G-spot stimulation by the man's penis. She may even be able to reach both clitoral and G-spot orgasms at the same time from this position.

Raised Feet Posture

This position needs a little bit of flexibility but it is also a sort of stretch, so if you ease into it you should be able to reach it in a few minutes after your body is warmed up.

The woman lies on her back and brings her knees to her chest, wrapping her arms around them, her body forming a small ball shape. The man kneels near her buttocks and enters her vagina from a kneeling position in front of her. Her vagina will be quite easily accessible because her legs are lifted at her chest. If the flexibility is there, the man can now lean forward with his upper body and with his own chest, he can hold her legs to her chest for her so that her hands are free. With her free hands, she can hold the back of his neck, pull his hair or caress his face, depending on what direction you want to go with this sexual encounter. From here, the man's penis can very easily meet the woman's G-spot because of its curve and this will make for an intense orgasm for both parties. The restriction of movement paired with the extreme closeness of their bodies is sure to make for some pent-up arousal that has no other way to be released than through a full-body orgasm.

The Supported Congress

This position is a different variety of a standing position than we have already seen, but can be done with more ease than some of the other standing varieties.

To get into this position, the man stands in front of a wall with the woman standing in front of him, facing him. The woman lifts one knee up and wraps her leg around one of the man's legs. The man can then slide his penis into her vagina, her leg raised to allow for deeper penetration and easier access. In standing positions, it may be more difficult to get the penetration right away but with some maneuvering and adjustments because of height differences, you will eventually get into a comfortable rhythm.

This position is a midway point to another Kamasutra position called The Suspended Congress, where the woman has both legs up and the man is holding them both under her knees and thrusting into her while holding her weight up. This position is quite difficult for the man, but if achieved it can lead to very deep penetration. The Supported Congress is a great place to start if you want to eventually try it with both legs up, as it is quite similar.

The Half-Pressed Position

This position is another midpoint to a more difficult Kamasutra position requiring a lot of flexibility, but this one is quite good even at this midway point! The woman's legs are spread wide and so it is very pleasurable for both of them.

The woman lies down on her back with her man kneeling in front of her. She stretches one leg straight out past him, besides his body and with the other leg, she bends her knee and places her foot on his chest. From here, he enters her vagina. The woman can move her hips up or down to give varying amounts of pressure to the man's penis for added pleasure for him. The stretching of her leg opens her clitoris up to potentially be stimulated by the base of his penis when he thrusts his hips and penetrates deeply into her. Having one foot planted on his chest keeps her legs open wide with every one of his thrusts in order to allow for deep penetration and clitoral stimulation.

The Yawning Position Variation

Have you ever heard of the term 'balls deep'? Have you ever wanted to try it? The Yawning Position creates the deepest possible penetration of any sexual position. In the classic yawning position, the woman puts her legs in the air and spreads her legs with her knees straight, forming a 'V' shape. The man kneels in front of her and puts his penis inside her from the front. This creates an intense sensation for both partners.

The variation of The Yawning Position that we are going to look at can begin when the woman is fully aroused and wet. The woman lies on her back and lifts her legs into the air with her knees straight. The man lies on top of her in a missionary-like position. She places her straight legs on the man's shoulders. He can then enter her vagina with his erect penis and thrust his hips forward for the deepest penetration. As I said, this position makes for the deepest possible vaginal penetration of any sexual position, and if the woman can manage it, she can slide her legs to the outer edges of the man's shoulders which will make for maximum depth of penetration as her legs will be as far spread as possible.

Afternoon Delight

Afternoon Delight is a nice position to try on a quiet Sunday after a long work week when you are both feeling tired and want a bit of lazy sex. You can start this position off with some lazy hand and finger play and then progress it to penetration in the same position if you are already cuddling and don't want to move around too much. This position is optimal for stoners and sleepyheads.

The man lies down on his side, his erect penis poking out in front of him. The woman lies on her back at a 90-degree angle to the man's body, halfway down near his genitals. She then bends her knees, lifts her legs and drapes them over the man's side, sliding her vagina towards him so it is close to his penis. He can move forward to meet her and slide his penis in her vagina. The woman can lie back and relax while the man thrusts his hips. This position can be done while you watch a tv show, while you are reading or while you are both half-asleep and want a little bit of Afternoon Delight. If this inspires you to try something more involved once you get into the mood, you can easily transition to Missionary or Doggy Style from here.

The Cross

The woman lies on her back with one leg extended straight into the air. The man kneels in front of her, straddling her leg that is extended on the bed and holds onto her other leg which is in the air. He can then move his body forward between her two legs until he is close enough to insert his penis into her vagina. He can hold her legs spread with his body, straddling one of them and placing the other one on his shoulder. By doing this, his hands will be free so that he can play with her clitoris, massage her breasts, rubbing his hands up and down her body or whatever they please. They can talk dirty to each other while looking at each other in the eyes and tell each other what they want done to them or what feels good.

The Plough

As the name suggests, this position is designed to look like a type of human plough, but I assure you, it is much sexier than it sounds. A good introduction for some of the more interesting and difficult positions, this one will get you both acquainted with the world of Kamasutra as it is known in today's pop culture.

You as the woman, lie face-down on the bed with your hips and legs sticking off the end and support yourself on your elbows. Your man stands on the floor beside the bed, his body positioned between your legs. He then lifts your lower half up by your hips and thighs and inserts his penis into your vagina, while supporting your legs the entire time. You can take a more passive role in this position, and he can adjust the angle he holds your legs at for maximum pleasure.

The Toad

This position is similar to The Toad (or The Frog) stretch that you probably used to do in gym class as a child. Facing the floor with bent knees spread wide to get those hips stretched. I bet you never thought that would help you in your sex life... But low and behold, turn that stretch over and you have The Toad position! I will explain in more detail as follows.

The woman lies on her back, bending her knees towards her chest and spreading her knees open wide. This opens her body up for easy penetration, clitoris access and maximum exposure of all of her pleasurable parts to her man's body that will be rubbing against them. The woman's entire vulva can be a pleasurable area if it is exposed to touch like the man's pelvis or hips rubbing it. This coupled with the clitoris being rubbed at the same time will drive her crazy. The man lies on top of her and slides his penis into her vagina, having lots of space for a deep penetration. In this position, the woman's clitoris can easily be stimulated from the thrusting motion of the man's body on top of hers or from the base of his penis when he comes as close to her as possible with each thrust. If the woman wants to take more control, once he is inside of her, she can wrap her legs around his waist and use them to pull his hips towards her along with his movement to increase the pressure and depth of his penetration.

The Peg

The Peg has a sexy name that implies pleasure and may even have you turned on already. This is a more difficult position, certainly more difficult to get yourselves into, but it comes with the reward of a great all-encompassing orgasm for both parties if it can be done.

The man lies on his side and the woman lies facing him on her side, with her head towards his feet. The woman will lift her knees towards her chest and place one of her legs underneath the man's legs and have the other on top of his legs. Essentially, she is hugging his legs with her entire body. She slides up so that her vulva is next to his penis. When aligned properly he can penetrate her and can achieve depth and control as she is positioned perfectly for his penis to enter her. The woman wraps her arms around his legs and he can use his hands and arms to help with his thrusting, or if she is comfortable, he can use his hands to stimulate her anal area with his fingers or a toy. The woman is positioned like this allows for all of her vulva to be open and accessible once again and this is what will lead to a stronger orgasm for her. The man being able to see all of her and to play with her anus will lead to a stronger orgasm for him.

Sex Games

Sex doesn't always have to be serious. Sex can be fun, too. In fact, laughter and a sense of play helps break the tension during new sexual experiences. Playing games and goofing around will bring you both out of your shell, allowing you to try new things and push each other's erotic boundaries comfortably.

Silent Sex

Sounds easy, right? Wrong. Try making love to your partner without making a sound. Do what you have to do: bite your lip, cover his mouth, and shove her face into a pillow...all is fair game.

To ramp up the stakes, whenever one of you makes a noise – the other person has to totally stop what they're doing.

You'll discover that when you're not allowed to express yourself verbally or vocally, you find another way to let that pleasure out through biting, squeezing, and desperately grabbing your partner to fuck you deeper.

Sex Dice

Your sexual experience is all up to fate with a roll of the dice.

Each set comes with two dice. One lists different activities like "lick", "tickle", "squeeze" and the other lists body parts like "nipples", "ass", "belly button".

This is a fun game to play with a glass of wine on the living room floor and watch where it leads.

Edging

When a vampire wants to turn human into a vampire, he must bite them without killing them. He must show extreme self-control and stop just before the human dies. You can think of Edging like this...without the whole death thing.

Edging is the act of coming so close to orgasm and then stopping. You repeat this over and over (3-4 times minimum) during the course of a few hours. When you finally let yourself or your partner cum...the orgasm will be one of the most intense you've ever had.

Make Bets with Dirty Wagers

Inject your sex life into everyday activities. When you're out and about, make sexy wagers on things like basketball games, whether or not it's going to rain, and how long it will take you to get home in this traffic.

The wages can be silly sexual things like "you have to lick peanut butter off of my nipples" or intense wagers like "you have to make me cum when we get home". You can one-up each other's wagers and set your own terms before you agree on the final bet.

To experiment with this challenge, pick a Sunday afternoon where the two of you spend the day together, taking turns setting wagers.

After the Sex Bucket List is complete, you might find yourselves carry this game on well into your future.

Porn Night

Take turns picking a porn- it doesn't matter the category. Start out with some categories neither of you watch on your own like MILF or Bondage to warm up- these are categories that you can both giggle about together and maybe get some new ideas. Go in with the mindset that this is going to be an entertaining activity together...while we all know that it's impossible not to get turned on during the process.

Eventually, start showing each other what you really like to watch...and see how long you can go without turning the night into your own porno.

The 10-Minute Rule

The dominant partner in this scenario sets a timer for 10 minutes. In those ten minutes, they tease their submissive partner relentlessly- nothing is off limits. The catch? The submissive partner is not allowed to touch the dominant partner until the timer goes off. But watch out, that timer will release a ravenous beast.

Strip Poker

Or Strip Chess. Or Strip Checkers. Or Strip Battle Ship. You can turn any game into a stripping game if you just believe in yourselves.

This kind of playful spirit brings out the flirt in both of you. The tease of watching clothes slowly coming off is wonderfully torturous. And that competitive edge will add a little spice to your dynamic.

If you want to step the game up one more level, you can make a rule that whomever is naked first receives a penalty of some slutty sex act or spankings

Weird Bonus Challenge: Tarzan and Jane

Bringing animal planet to the bedroom, things are about to get rough in this male pursuit/female resistance game. Secure ropes or ties to the corners of the bed. The goal is for Tarzan to wrestle Jane into submission, getting both of her hands and legs tightly secured. Jane's job is to resist.

While this 'Tarzan and Jane' might sound rapey, with a partner that you trust, this game can be so hot. It starts out playful and funny, then all of a sudden, your inner animal is unleashed, and you end up having the best rough and angry sex.

Finished the Challenge?

You dirty kids...

 But hey, you're not done yet.

Now both of you need to scan through the past 100 sexual experiences and pick your top 5 sexual experiences.

Which naughty acts did you play over and over again in your head at work? Which one made you cum the hardest? Which one do you want to try again until you can perfect it?

Write them down and take turns reading them to each other, one by one.

Top 5 Sex Challenges

Her Top 5

1. _____

2. _____

3. _____

4. _____

5. _____

His Top 5

1. _____

2. _____

3. _____

4. _____

5. _____

Your New Naughty Challenge?

To explore the sexual experiences above, weaving them in your normal sex life…that is, if you can consider your sex life "normal" anymore.

Cut out 16 pieces of paper – 8 pieces each. Use each slip of paper to write your Top 5 sex challenges and 3 sex challenges that you'd like to try again.

Fold the papers and put them into a decorative bowl or a fish bowl. Twice a week for 8 weeks, you'll take turns picking a piece of paper out of the jar and acting out whatever is on that slip of paper.

Important: Designate two solid nights a week to do this. Write it on a calendar and do not skip it. Prioritize each other. Prioritize your sex life.

Advice for Beginners

Having sex for the first time can be an exciting and nervous experience full of anticipation. It involves a wide range of emotions. Once you become familiar with sex, even if on a basic level, you will begin to learn what brings you and your partner pleasure. It could be through a certain touch or sensation. Try to see how your lover reacts when you kiss or touch them in certain away. One of the most important ways to ease into sexual intimacy is through a gentle session of foreplay. This can be subtle, beginning with light kissing and touching, showing and exchanging signs of affection. During this phase, you may notice a decrease in anxiety and begin to experience signs of arousal. An erection is one of the initial signs in men, while women may feel their labia engorge and swell.

There may be slight wetness or moistening in the genital area, as well as heightened sensitivity to touch and sound. During this phase, the mutual attraction intensifies, which creates a transition to sex.

The Challenges of Sexual Education in Society

In many cultures and societies, sex education is considered taboo and avoided as much as possible. Even in countries where there is a more relaxed approach to the concept of sex and where it is introduced into the education system or tackled within the family, there still exists a gap between learning the fundamentals of biology and how to experience the pleasures of sexual activity. Sex education in most schools, for example, centers on the prevention of STIs (sexually transmitted infections), the concept of sexual arousal, and how the reproductive system works. In some progressive school systems, the curriculum has a broader spectrum of education to include all sexual orientations. These schools also have a more accepting approach to sexual and gender identity. However, there still exists a significant amount of resistance against a general openness to sexuality, and people are not generally taught how to enjoy and seek pleasure during sex.

Some family and marital arrangements have a heavy reliance on traditional practices that hold on to strict male and female roles. They place a more dominant role on men, with the expectation that women will always be sexually compliant and available even when there is no explicit consent. This power dynamic places men in a more commanding position where women's sexual needs and wants are suppressed.

On the other hand, men are expected to take on a traditional "leadership" role, which doesn't come with the goal of giving women pleasure or helping them achieve pleasure together as a couple. In relationships where there is both a lack of sexual education and mutual connection, sexual intimacy can be a major challenge, often done out of necessity and starting a family. Thus, it is less about pleasure and pleasing each other.

As some people break away from their traditional roles in marriage and intimate relationships, they realize there is much to learn from each other, especially on how to express their desires, bond with each other, and experience the joy of sex together.

While many people hold on to traditional views of marriage and sex, it is important to recognize the importance of learning the value of pleasure: how to please ourselves and our partners. This will only become easier for people once the stigma of sexual openness and communication fades away over time, allowing more discussion and direct communication about sex and how we can enjoy it.

Important Facts About Sex Everyone Should Know

Learning about sex goes beyond the basics of biology. It goes beyond responding to various cues and states of arousal. There are a lot of interesting facts to know about sex. If you are new to sex or less experienced, you will find that the early stages are a combination of learning from what you hear, read, and experience first-hand. If you are more knowledgeable than your partner, you can provide more guidance. However, care should always be taken so that both of you feel comfortable and willing to engage. The following important facts are vital and interesting, and they should be considered before you decide to engage with your partner.

1. Consent should be explicit.

When it comes to sex, a simple "Yes, I want to make love" is not always the way we consent or agree to have sex. When one partner initiates intimacy, the other may appear interested at first and then may hesitate later on. The reasons can vary, from changing their mind to simply not being interested in the moment. When there is the slightest doubt, it is important to establish whether consent is present, and make sure both of you are completely 100 percent willing without any reservations. There should be explicit consent, which means you and your partner should be fully in agreement and enthusiastic about it.

2. Sex is not going to be the same experience every time.

Some sessions will be groundbreaking and exciting, leaving you wanting more. On other occasions, sex is less than thrilling and may not bring both or either partner to orgasm. This can be a result of various things — e.g., personal trauma in life, stress from family or work, or simply not feeling completely engaged or aroused in the experience. This is perfectly normal. It would be unusual to have ideal sex each and every time, as this is unrealistic. Do not expect this to happen always. It is important to be realistic, and accept the fact that, on some occasions, the spark may not be present. Be patient, and you will find that the best experiences will return again.

3. Long sessions of sex do not equate to better quality, and short, quick sex does not always have to be negative either.

It really depends on the couple and the circumstances. For example, in the morning, a quick session of early sex may be brief but highly passionate and satisfying. In fact, both lovers may be familiar enough with each other to bring about orgasm within a short time span, and then they go their separate ways for work and other daily activities. A longer session in a rushed morning would not accommodate their schedule. On the other hand, a slower, deeper intimacy in the evening hours can be satisfying in a completely different way, allowing both partners to experience more of each other.

4. Erection does not happen instantly every time, and when it does, it may occur when it is least expected.

A man may find himself with an erection in the morning during a shower or as he's getting ready for breakfast. A woman, on the other hand, may feel aroused during regular activities, such as attending a conference or running errands. When sex is initiated, it may take time to achieve an erection and natural arousal, even where both lovers are ready and excited to begin.

5. Lubrication is good for everyone.

It is wonderful how our bodies can create our own wetness, though it is best to add a bit of natural lubricant to your sexual encounter to avoid dryness and irritation later. There are various brands to choose from. You can also choose a variety of flavors and/or scents. There is also a choice between a more sensitive and natural fluid versus a more standard one. Take time to shop around with your partner to determine which one works best for both of you.

6. Moving from one position to another during sex is not always a simple task.

It mainly depends on your flexibility. Try new poses or positions, and switch them up every now and then. Some moves are going to take some practice, even exercise, to get them just right. Some positions may require your partner to lend you a hand, or you may need to help them steady their balance or ease slowly into a new pose. It may not look and feel glamorous, but it will be fun just the same!

7. Using protection is important, and knowing how to use it is vital.

Condoms are the most commonly used and preferred method of birth control and protection against STIs (sexually transmitted diseases). They are important early in the relationship. However, learning how to use a condom for the first time can be frustrating, and it often causes friction if not lubricated well. Condoms are not all created equally. Some brands may boast high sensitivity, while others are more durable and already lubricated, making it easier to put on. To avoid potential breakage and to ensure your experience is not spoiled, make sure you have a few condoms handy, just in case. Read the instructions carefully and take it slowly at first until you become used to the procedure. Remember that your partner can be helpful and give you much-needed support and assistance to get your session underway. There are creative and fun ways of putting on a condom, and this can fit easily into foreplay, making the experience much more enjoyable.

8. Sex is good for your health, and it is a form of exercise.

The more often you engage, the more calories you will burn. It is great for the heart and your body in general. Sex itself is a euphoric experience, causing a release of endorphins in the body, which reduces the likelihood of depression, anxiety, and other disorders. The frequency of sex varies from one couple to another, and while it is often more often at the beginning of the relationship, a routine will eventually become established. Even if you are engaging twice a week, there are fantastic benefits to your health and well-being.

9. Smoking can have a negative impact on your sex life.

Not only is smoking bad for your health, but it is also associated with lower rates of arousal and a decline in the strength of an erection. It can also affect endurance, making it difficult for the smoker to last longer in the bedroom, especially where there are respiratory conditions involved. If you currently smoke, consider quitting or taking steps to decrease the amount you use, as this will make a major improvement over time.

10. Orgasm is not going to happen every time you have sex.

You can have a hot and passionate session with your partner and not achieve a climax. Likewise, your partner can experience the same; it happens for both men and women. It can cause feelings of disappointment and insecurity. It is normal for this to occur sometimes, even between health-loving couples.

11. The more you communicate, the better your sex life will be.

Many people avoid talking about certain topics, including sex and intimacy. When communication breaks down, it can lead to a lot of misunderstandings, hurt, and avoidance. Intimacy can eventually break down until it reaches the point where it is no longer a part of a couple's life. Once this happens, it can lead to marital or relationship breakdown as well. Keeping the conversation alive is the best way to enjoy all that your relationship can provide.

There are many other facts about sex that you can learn in a variety of ways. One of the best ways to get familiar with your body and to engage with your partner is through open dialogue and discussion about a variety of concerns, including your fantasies and desires (Gordon, 2018).

Five Uncommon Facts That Can Improve Your Sex Life

Getting comfortable with your partner will not only help improve your sex life but will also give you the confidence to ask questions and better understand how you can mutually pleasure each other. Exploring various techniques and ideas and having openness to doing so has a major impact on the success of your love life and how well it will develop over time. Couples who explore and communicate about sex without reservation tend to lead healthier, happier lives in general, not just in the bedroom.

There are a few unexpected ideas and facts that make a positive impact on your sex life. Some of these facts dispel myths about sex, giving us a different perspective on how to enjoy our love life. They also create a healthy outlook about sex and how we engage with our partner and ourselves.

1. The most sexual part of our body is our brain.

The onset of arousal and the creation of sexual fantasies begin here. It is our mind that plays the most significant role in how we experience lovemaking and how we connect with our partner. Our perception (the signals our body and mind process and send throughout our body during foreplay and sex) sets the stage for a spectacular series of sensations. Alternatively, when our thoughts or impressions about a specific scenario are negative, it affects our body's response. For example, if we feel hesitant about pursuing a specific technique with our partner or lack trust in them for some reason, even the usual pleasurable event of lovemaking can be unenjoyable. This is because your mind isn't completely involved or relaxed for the experience. When we feel connected in mind and body, sex only gets better over time.

2. Women only orgasm 20 percent of the time during sex.

This is usually because some men believe women can achieve climax with vaginal sex alone, whereas this is not often the case. In fact, most women need clitoral stimulation or oral sex to bring themselves to orgasm. In some positions, it is possible for both men and women to reach orgasm together, which can be incredibly pleasurable, though it can also take practice and time to achieve. It is also advantageous for couples to explore various forms of arousal, as well as positions that include oral sex. This will greatly increase the chances of orgasm for women and can help men as well.

3. Men also fake orgasms.

145

Women often admit to this, though men have been found to do this as well and often for the same reason: they want to please their partner or give the impression that they have been adequately satisfied. This may be a way for men to assure their partner that they are able to reach orgasm quickly and to convey confidence. For women, there are several reasons. Like men, they want to show their satisfaction or at least convince their partner of it. Faking an orgasm gives the other person the satisfaction of being able to bring their partner to climax and, therefore, boosts their ego or confidence. The problem with this technique is dishonesty. Faking an experience you should want to enjoy is not giving you any real pleasure, while at the same time, it gives your partner the wrong impression of what works for you.

4. Headaches and pain can often disappear or subside during sex.

The popular excuse for declining sex, "Not tonight, I have a headache," is usually joked about as a means to avoid intimacy or skip sex. In reality, such an excuse could mean something more, especially if it is a recurring phrase (or something similar). There may be a hidden discomfort associated with sex that your partner may not feel like explaining, though they may be more direct and open with patience and understanding. It is important to communicate to find out the real reasons for lack of intimacy and to gently approach the topic so as not to push or pressure your partner to explain everything, especially if there is (or are) reason(s) why they may not feel up to it (Hubby, 2017).

5. Many women masturbate, though they tend not to discuss it as freely or widely as men, mostly due to societal expectations and ideals.

Even where women have made great strides forward in freedom, including sexual expression and liberation, there are still items considered less favorable when broached by a woman than a man. Masturbation is one of these topics, as well as sex in general. However, this is changing, and women are becoming more vocal and expressive than ever. Masturbation, or self-pleasure, should never be a source of shame, whether you enjoy it for yourself or mutually with your partner (Carson, 2017).

Sex Positions for Beginners

It is important to understand that while some positions may be great for you your partner may not love them. So, trying different things and having an Arsenal of different sex positions to try is advantageous in having excellent sexual sessions. Here again, you need to be open to experimentation. Trying out different positions can lead you to a whole new world of ecstasy that you have never experienced.

Let's start out by looking at some of the most basic sex positions that can be accomplished while laying down and how to actually make them happen. However, they may surprise you once you actually give them a try. So, don't feel as if the basics aren't good enough as often times they absolutely are.

The first position that we would like to look at is the face to face position. To accomplish this both parties will be laying on their sides. You'll be facing each other. The female will be slightly higher on the bed than her male counterpart. This is so that her hips are above his. One of her legs will wrap around the top of him and the other one should be laid down straight. Sometimes this can feel a bit awkward but with practice, it feels truly great.

This is a fantastic position for beginners because it helps you to gain comfort with your partner. It is a very intimate position that will allow deeper levels of penetration. The closeness of this position also helps both to relax and enjoy the experience.

We have one of the most common positions, missionary style. This is done by the female lying flat on her back and the male on top of her. The female's legs can be in a variety of different positions. Sometimes, she will lay them down flat on the bed while other times she may wrap them around her partner's waist. This simply comes down to what is most comfortable. Other people prefer to have their knees bent so that their feet are flat on the bed and their knees are facing the ceiling.

Missionary position is basic but essential for beginners. It is one of our go-to moves. It allows for different positioning which can help both parties achieve orgasm more easily. It tends to be very comfortable for both the man and the

147

woman. You will be facing each other, and this will allow you to focus on the level of intimacy that you are exuding. Additionally, it will make it easy to communicate what your needs are if the position needs to change slightly.

Spooning is another basic position that offers a great deal of satisfaction for both parties. To accomplish this, you will lay in the spoon position. The female's hips should be above her partners. The Top leg will need to be lifted slightly so that penetration can occur. Sometimes this feels a bit awkward and you may need to adjust your positioning to find a good level of comfort.

This position is fantastic for beginners because it allows for stimulation to the females G-spot quite easily. It can be very comfortable once you find the right fit. You won't have to worry about doing a whole lot of work but both parties will be able to move fairly easily. The involvement of both people is appreciated on both sides and it is likely that you will fall in love with this basic position.

Now that we have looked at some awesome positions that you can use while laying down will move on to some sitting positions. Sitting positions can allow for deeper levels of penetration which can, in turn, offer higher levels of stimulation for both parties. Sitting positions are usually very easy to achieve and are a natural go-to for couples that are inexperienced, as well as, experienced.

The first position that we are going to discuss is a combination of a lying down and sitting position. This position is most commonly referred to as the cowgirl style. To accomplish it, the male will lay flat on his back with his legs stretched out in front of him. The woman will climb on Top and straddle him. How she chooses to position her legs should be in whatever position is the most comfortable. From here she will have the ability to take control and ride her male counterpart.

Beginners love this position because it is easy to accomplish. It is important to note that if the female puts her feet flat on the bed with her knees facing the ceiling or the wall it will be a bit difficult to do this for very long. The motion will be difficult on her thigh muscles. However, this can be combated by putting one shin down on the bed and leaving the other in the upward position. It provides great leverage and an excellent level of penetration. Additionally, it will allow the woman to ride the man's penis in a way that stimulates her G-spot.

You can modify this position in a variety of different ways. To make it a true sitting position you simply need to change the position of the man. Rather than him lying on his back have him sit with his back leaning against a solid surface. He can bend his knees or leave them straight just depending on what feels best for both parties. From there the female is going to do the exact same thing as stated above.

It is important to note that some women will find this position to be intimidating if they're lacking in, experience. This is due to the fact that they are extremely exposed. However, as long as you have an intimate and trusting connection with your partner it is definitely worth giving this position a try. It can lead to excellent levels of stimulation an ecstasy.

You can alter the cowgirl into another position by simply turning the female around. This is referred to as a reversed cowgirl. It provides a different stimulation to both the man and the woman. This is due to the fact that the underside of the man's penis will now be rubbing the front wall of the woman's vagina. This type of stimulation can be fantastic for reaching climax and providing mind-blowing orgasms.

Now we're going to move on to a couple of basic kneeling positions that you can easily enter into during sexual encounters. Kneeling positions can be truly amazing for both parties. This is due to the fact that you tend to have a good amount of movement and deeper levels of penetration in positions where one or both parties are kneeling.

The first position that we want to look at is the doggie style. This is one of the most popular positions for inexperienced, as well as, experienced people. Many find that this is one of their favorite positions because of the level of penetration and movement that can be experienced. In addition, men tend to like the view of their ladies from behind.

To accomplish the doggie style position is fairly simple. The woman will need to be on her hands and knees or on her forearms and knees. The man will approach her from behind. Her knees should be about shoulder-width apart so that her man can kneel between them. He will then enter her from behind. More often than not the man will hold on to the woman's hips which will give him some control over the speed and power of his thrust. However, this position is also good if the woman wants to take control.

There are different variations of the doggie style position. Sometimes, the woman will lay flat on her stomach and the man will kneel over top of her. This can be a bit more challenging than a basic doggie style position, but it is also very exciting. It will make the female feel tighter around her man's member and heighten the level of pleasure that both parties experience.

Now we move on to some basic standing positions. There are many variations of standing positions that are very easy to accomplish. However, you need to be aware that some standing positions are very difficult to participate in for long periods of time. Don't get discouraged if you can't participate in standing positions for a long time, just keep at it and it will get easier the more experienced you are.

The first position we are going to look at is a combination of standing and kneeling positions. In this position, the woman will kneel on the bad like she would in a doggie style position. The difference is the man will be standing. He will approach the woman from behind and place his legs between hers. This will give him excellent leverage. He will also be able to grab her by the hips and control the speed and thrust at which intercourse is performed.

This position is extremely easy to accomplish and exceptionally pleasurable for both parties. He will be able to play with depth to tease her and truly provide her with a variety of sensations. More than likely both parties will be able to participate in this position for a decent amount of time as it is not physically demanding.

Another standing position that is great well require the use of a chair. Both parties will be standing. The woman will face forward and lean over bracing herself on the chair. She will spread her legs so that they are shoulder with apart. It is important to note that if you are dealing with a partner who is much taller or shorter than you, you may need to stand up on your toes or kneel slightly. The man will then approach her from behind with his legs between hers wow he enters her. This position can be a little bit tired so, if you can't do it for very long don't get discouraged.

It is important to note that not everybody will be able to accomplish it. There are a couple of variations but to accomplish this position the woman will have her back against the wall. You will be face to face with your partner. She will want to raise one or both of her legs so that they are around her partner's waist. The man will then position himself to be able to penetrate her. It will require a decent amount of strength from the man as he will be supporting quite uh a lot of the woman's weight. This is especially true if she is intending unwrapping both legs around his waist. This position provides an insane level of penetration. There will not be a ton of movement, but the sensations can allow both parties to reach orgasm quite easily.

Once you have experimented with these sex positions, you'll be able to move into other ones. Understand that there are hundreds of different positions that you can try out. We have only given you the tip of the iceberg. There are many other basic positions that are easy to accomplish. In addition, there are more advanced ones that will take some practice. When you're comfortable with your sexual partner experimenting with sex positions becomes extremely easy. Additionally, it helps to heighten the experience and keep things interesting if you are in a long-term relationship.

How to Discover Your Sexual Fantasies and Fetishes

You are now aware of what sexual fantasies and fetishes are, but you may now be wondering if you have any personally. Everyone has sexual acts or themes that turn them on, but you must get in touch with this part of yourself in order to find out what your personal ones are.

First, though, we will look at some specific types of sexual fantasies so that you can get an idea of what you are looking to discover. Under the umbrella of sexual fantasies is included the following, among others;

• Roleplay

If your sexual fantasy or kink is role play, you likely become aroused when you imagine playing a certain role in the bedroom with your partner like a homeowner, and he is a plumber coming to fix your pipes.

• Domination and Submission

If your kink or fetish is domination and submission, you likely become turned on by playing a certain role in bed- either being dominated by your partner or being dominant over them.

• Specific Sexual Acts

Your kink could also be related to specific sexual acts. These can include spanking, hair pulling or Piss Play

There are so many things that can be included in these categories and so many more categories of their own. Many categories will overlap and cross over each other. For example, a police and convict role play fantasy could cross over into domination and submission play as well. By getting an idea of what is out there, you can begin to explore what you like the idea of and what you don't like sexually.

Look Inward

The first part of determining anything about yourself is to look inward and get in touch with your inner thoughts, feelings, and desires. If you are not used to looking inward and examining your feelings, it may take some practice and getting used to before you are able to determine what your fantasies, kinks or fetishes are. In order to get in touch with your feelings and thoughts, set aside some time to get quiet with your own mind.

Start to begin letting yourself fantasize about sex in general and see where this takes you. The main thing here is to let your mind go wherever it goes without trying to control it. By allowing it to drift anywhere and everywhere, you can begin to see what lies hidden in your subconscious mind.

Avoid Self-Judgement

Self-judgement can sometimes creep in when you become sexually aroused by something that is deemed unacceptable in society. When you have a sexual fantasy, it is important to remember that there need not be any shame involved- having a specific sexual fantasy does not mean that you would actually act it out in real life. Because of this, you can put your self-judgments aside and enjoy your fantasy without thinking of yourself as some sort of deviant.

Masturbation

As you are giving yourself a quiet moment to explore your mind and your desires, you may find yourself becoming sexually aroused. This is great, as it means that you have found some things that are sexually exciting to you. As this happens, you can begin to touch yourself if you wish. Masturbation is a healthy part of anybody's sex life, and there is no shame in this either.

As you begin touching yourself, allow your mind to explore your sexual fantasies, kinks, and fetishes more deeply as you become aroused. By doing this, you will be much more able to let your subconscious take over you. This is where your desires and your deeper wishes are held. Most of the time, these remain in your subconscious unbeknownst to you. It is only when you are able to access this part of your mind that you can become aware of what lies there. By doing this, you allow yourself to unlock a different level of sexual adventure and exploration. This is something that you can then share with your partner, and they can begin to know you on a much deeper level.

Research

By doing a little bit of research, you can figure out what is out there, what is encompassed by these terms, and what you specifically find pleasure in.

You can do research in different ways. You could explore different articles on the internet of The Most Common Sexual Fantasies or Stories of the Weirdest Sexual Fetishes. You could also look at different types of porn as there is an unlimited amount of porn available on the internet, and within this, there is a wide array of fantasies and fetishes included. The one thing to keep in mind when looking at porn is that you want to make sure you are not taking the sex you see in porn as reality. While the ideas of fantasies and fetishes can be informative to you, porn can also set unrealistic expectations for viewers related to things such as average penis size or breast size as well as how to please a woman. As long as you keep this in mind, porn can be a useful tool for exploring kinks and fetishes you never knew existed.

Even if you only find out what you are not interested in sexually, this research will still have proven to be informative.

Talk to People

Talking to your friends or people who you meet that are open about their sex lives can be another great source of information for you. The benefit to this as well is that it can give you a more realistic view of these things than you may be able to find on the internet.

You could begin by asking people about their sexual fantasies, or if they are aware of them at all. You can ask them also if they have shared these with their partners. By initiating a conversation like this, you can learn a lot about other people and their sexual fantasies or kinks.

Once you have begun to explore your sexual fantasies, kinks, and fetishes, you will be able to begin exploring them. Exploring your fetishes is a lifelong process, as your likes and desires may change over time. Once you have found out how to be in touch with this part of yourself, you can continue to let it inform your sex life forever.

How to Discuss Your Fetishes with Your Partner

It may seem quite intimidating opening up to your partner about your kinks or fetishes or even your sexual fantasies as they are very personal to you.

You may fear judgment or disgust, and you may fear that your partner will not be interested in taking part in your sexual fantasies or fetishes.

You may be self-conscious about what turns you on and unsure of how your partner will feel about it. If you have been in this relationship for a while now and you still have not conversed these with your partner, your anxiety about bringing them up has likely only increased with time. At the beginning of a relationship, you may be hesitant to bring up things that please you that you deem unusual or not-so-vanilla. This is completely understandable, and we will discuss how to bring these topics up in conversation, regardless of how long you have been in your current relationship or marriage. The other reason could be that you have just recently discovered a new kink, and that is okay as well. If you have never acted on them before, talking to your partner about trying them can be done as a conversation about mutual exploration.

Keep in mind that many of us think our kinks are odd and embarrassing, but they are probably not as off the wall as you think they are. Fetishes may also be embarrassing to discuss, but if you are so into a certain thing that you require it in order to be pleased, your partner will surely be interested. As your partner, they are invested in your pleasure and should always be wondering how best to please you. So how do you initiate a conversation about your kinks or fetishes with your partner or spouse? The key is entering the conversation with the intention of not only explaining to them your own desires but of listening to and understanding your partner's kinks and fetishes as well.

Begin by asking your partner if there is anything that they have been interested in trying in the bedroom, or if there is anything new that they have wanted to explore sexually with you. This will initiate an open dialogue about sex and desires in general. Listen with an open mind. Your partner may be into something that you are also into! Then, they will likely ask you the same question back. Explain to them that you have wanted to try something new in your sex life with them. Explain to them what it is and how it makes you feel. Maybe you have explored this in a past relationship, and maybe that is where you first discovered this specific thing that turns you on. Maybe you have never tried it with someone else, and you would like to begin exploring it with them. If this person loves you, they care about your pleasure. Even if they may have reservations about trying something new, they are likely to be open to giving it a shot for you. Be open to exploring your kink or fetish at a beginner level if your partner has never tried it before. Sex is all about comfort and pleasure and as long as you are both feeling these two things, preferably by meeting in the middle, a good time is sure to be had by all. When explaining your kink to them, be sure to explain how it makes you feel and how it could make them feel. Explain what exactly you enjoy about it. Explain how exactly you enjoy it and what role you like to take in it. Do you like to be the dominant one? The submissive one? Allow them to ask questions and be curious. the ability to have an open conversation about sex in a relationship is essential to having a positively evolving sex life as your relationship grows and progresses. You want your sex life to grow and change along with the both of you.

We will now look at an example of this and how this conversation may go for you, in order for you to feel more secure when bringing this up. For example, say your kink is rough sex. You and your partner may have been having soft, gentle, and loving sex up until this point because you know that that is what they like, but you have learned through a past relationship that you love rough sex. You may not have tried this or brought it up in conversation before because you were afraid that your partner would have been turned off or afraid. In order to bring this up to them in conversation, you can begin by saying something like, "I used to get very turned on by having rough sex, and I would like to try it with you."

How to Try New Fantasies and Fetishes for the First Time

When talking to your partner about your fetishes, they will likely be open-minded and willing to try it with you. This is great! In order to do this for the first time, there will be some things to keep in mind.

New Fantasy, Kink, or Fetish for Both People

If you have just discovered a new fetish or a new kink that you wish to try and you have conferred this with your partner, you can now begin to introduce this into your sex life. The positive thing about neither of you have done it before is that it can be an experience that you share with one another. By doing this, you can both evaluate as you go and decide what you like and what you dislike. For example, if you are wishing to try out a role play, you can begin by getting into the roles and using dirty talk as your characters, while ensuring that you have a safe word to use just in case someone becomes uncomfortable. A safeword is a predetermined word that you or your partner can say when one of you wishes to put the play aside and become yourselves for a time. You can use this to tell your partner that you wish to stop, to change something or to tell them something out of character. This can be used for any kink, fetish, or fantasy that you are playing out.

New Fantasy, Kink, or Fetish for Your Partner Only

If you have experience with the kink, fetish, or fantasy, but your partner does not, we will look at how to try this with your partner for the first time here.

If you are bringing up your fetish with your partner and this fetish is rough sex, there are many ways that you can begin to introduce this into your sex life with your partner without going straight to BDSM, as they may be a little afraid in the beginning and wish to ease into it, though they are open-minded. This is completely okay. There are many degrees of roughness in sex, and it will be easy to start out by just dipping your toes in the world of rough sex to see how your partner feels about it. You can explain this to them as well. Once they are comfortable with the idea and are wanting to try it with you, you will need to take the lead. Your partner will probably not know where to start, and you will lead them through it for their first few times. To teach them as you go, try using dirty talk to make it sexier than if you just gave them a lesson in kink like a lecture at school. Begin by explaining to them whether you enjoy being in the position of masochist (pleasure from pain inflicted on you) or sadist (pleasure from inflicting pain on another person). For example, you may like having your hair pulled or having your partner dig their nails into your back when you make them feel good.

Begin by having sex as you usually would, and when it comes time that you would like it to get a little rougher, tell your partner (using dirty talk) what you want them to do. Say something like the following; "pull my hair baby" or "spank me like you're punishing me". This will make your directions sexy and fitting for the mood. Your partner may be afraid to hurt you if they do not have experience with rough sex. You can assure them before you begin that they will not be hurting you, but in fact, they will be making you feel more pleasure than usual. They will likely be excited by this possibility. This may be enough for the first time, but be sure to communicate in order to find this out. Every person is different so every person's comfort level will be different. Your partner may get into it and end up loving it just as much as you do. By beginning in this way, you can go a little further each time you have sex, and in this way, both people's comfort and enjoyment are considered.

Have Fun and Play Dirty

Aside from a penis, a tongue, or fingers, a vibrator can be a woman's best friend. If you're a woman that doesn't have a vibrator (you poor, deprived thing!), you might want to consider getting one. Not only is it a great masturbation tool and a fine stress reliever, but it's also a wonderful way to share a sexual experience with your partner. Vibrators come in a variety of different shapes, sizes, styles, etc. You can get the old school, white plastic model, or you can go for the ultra-realistic looking dildo in the shape and size of your favorite male porn star.

How to get the best out of it

Some people view sex toys as something that is for those who have wild kinks or those who cannot perform without assistance of some sort. In reality, though, sex toys are designed to increase and enhance pleasure for anyone. By using sex toys, you do not have to engage in anything wild or anything that you are uncomfortable with. You are also not admitting that you have a sexual problem by using a sex toy.

One of the ways in which sex toys can improve your sex life is that they allow you to focus on one area of the body while the sex toy takes care of pleasure in another. For example, a sex toy that is designed to pleasure a woman's clitoris will do so while you can focus on her nipples or her vagina.

Finding the right toy

In order to choose the right sex toy for yourself, there are a couple of questions that you would need to answer first.

- Is this toy to be used alone during masturbation?

- Is it to be used with a partner?

- Is it to be used with multiple partners?

- Is it to be used for all of the above or two of the above?

- Do you want it to have a vibrating function?

- An insertion function?

- Will you use it anally?

- Vaginally?

- Both?

- Do you want it to be customizable (depending on your mood or the partner you are with)?

Once you establish this, you will be able to narrow down your search. Answering all of these questions will help you to determine which type of sex toy is right for you (and your partner).

Sex position and sex toys

Once you've got your first four sex toys ready, it's time to combine this with some sex positions and begin exploring just how much pleasure the introduction of something new can bring. Of course, you can start getting a little more adventurous later once both partners are comfortable with the idea of using these toys in the bedroom. Until then, these positions will serve as a good first step to test the waters:

The Missionary with Vibrator

Time to get back to basics once more as you slowly familiarize each other with the use of these sex toys. The woman will be lying down on her back on the bed, relaxed and ready. The man starts off slow and gentle, locating her clitoris with his fingers. Turn the vibrator on a low buzz, slowly bring it between her legs and place it so that it lightly touches her clitoris. The man then watches her facial expressions change as he tries varying amounts of pressure and speed settings of the vibrator. Occasionally take her by surprise by slipping a finger inside her vagina and find her G-spot while the vibrator is still going. Listen to her moans of desire for your cues to help her reach intense levels of pleasure. Adjust the speed when you're ready, increasing the speed as the woman gets wetter and wetter.

Doggy Style with The Strap-On

The Doggy position, when combined with a strap-on creates a mecca of pleasure. This time, however, it is the man who is going to be in the Doggy position while the woman wears the strap on and do what you normally would do in this position. Be careful when playing with the man's anus, and don't forget to use lots of lube for this one.

Seated Sex Position with the Vibrating Cock Ring

With the Cock Ring positioned at the base of the man's penis, vibrating and ready, the man sits in a chair while the woman sits on his lap, facing him with her legs around his waist and behind you. Have her stand up slightly, so she is hovering before she lowers herself onto the vibrating penis. Work together to move her body up and down on your penis. She can rotate her hips slightly backward, and the vibrating ring should stimulate her clitoris. The vibration of the ring will give her intense pleasure, and this position is ideal for a great male orgasm and a great female orgasm too.

Masturbation

Man's secret pleasure point

Male masturbation is described as the act of a man pleasuring himself by either touching or stimulating his penis, nipples, testicles, and other erogenous zones in his body. These self-pleasuring techniques usually carry on to the point of ejaculation or orgasm, and it is done purely to satisfy his sexual pleasure. This can be done either solo or when you're in private or as part of the foreplay leading up to sex with their partner, although most of the time, masturbation typically happens when the man is alone. As a man, masturbation can help you deal with anxieties, understand your sexual preferences, your body, improve your endurance during sex and generally keeps you happy.

Woman's secret pleasure point

Masturbation can be just as life-changing for a woman's sex life as it can be for a man. Many women struggle with body issues and poor self-image, but masturbation is a way of overcoming that and learning to love your body as it is. When you know how to pleasure yourself, it makes it easier to guide your partner about what they need to go to take your orgasms to the next level. Self-love is important for a woman because it can deeply affect your intimacy with your partner when you're not comfortable in your own skin. If you haven't spent a lot of time pleasuring yourself before this, it's never too late to start.

First, get to know your body better by holding a mirror between your legs to see what your partner sees when they are touching you or giving you oral sex. Take a good look at what you look like down there. This is you. This is your body. Now, start to feel around a little bit, massaging your vulva and locating your clitoris. Play around the area and observe the way your body responds to the touch. Some areas will feel oh so good while others will feel very, VERY good. You want to keep the sensation going on the "very good" areas.

Hand tricks to give extreme pleasure

Masturbation is often thought of as a solo act, but it could be surprisingly pleasurable to do this with your partner. Masturbation is an intimate thing and sharing this moment with someone you care about can bring you closer together as a couple. Mutual masturbation can be an incredible moment shared between you and your partner. For the man, watching his partner masturbate is probably high on his sexual wish list. It may not be as high on the list for the woman, but you may be surprised at how arousing it could be. As a bonus, you may each learn something new about your partner's arousal process. Some women may never even have seen a man ejaculate in real life other than is watched in porn films. Men, ejaculating in front of your partner is a very intimate act, and surprisingly enough, many women find it arousing not only physically but mentally and emotionally.

Face-to-Face

This position can be pulled off in a few ways, depending on how you and your partner like to do it. Begin by lying down on your side, facing your partner, and gazing into their eyes. The closer you are, the greater the intimacy and intensity of the moment. Touch yourself the way you would if you were masturbating alone and watch your partner's face start to change as they pleasure themselves too. It's a great time to throw in some dirty talk here. Keep this going until you both climaxes, perhaps even try attempting to orgasm at the same time.

Don't Ask

Instead of asking for sex, show your partner that you're in the mood instead. This tip works best for women, and without saying a word, position yourself provocatively comfortably and make sure he's got a good view. Place two fingers in an inverted V straddling your clitoris. This hand position is good for encouraging your orgasm. Throw yourself into your masturbation session with abandon and watch his face start to change as continues watching you pleasure yourself.

Stimulating His Testicles

This secret is key to giving your man some of the best orgasms of his life. This secret is in the testicles and knowing how to use them as a secret weapon of pleasure. Cup your partner's testicles gently and begin stroking them softly. Hold them and very lightly pull them towards you (be gentle here because his testicles will be sensitive to your touch). To double the pleasure, give him fellatio while you do this, it's going to drive him crazy as the stimulation of both his penis and his balls at the same time will make it hard for him not to finish right then and there. The warmth and moisture of your mouth around his penis, along with his testicles being gently rubbed will lead straight to orgasmic bliss.

Spice it up with dirty talks

What to say and when

That sometimes difficult, but always necessary sex conversation is what we are going, to begin with. This conversation can be difficult to work up to, especially if you have not had many conversations like this outside of dirty talk in the bedroom. What I'm talking about is an adult conversation where you ask them what they want, what they need, and what they like and dislike. This conversation is one that should happen in every relationship when you first begin a sexual relationship and should be revisited over and over again throughout the course of your relationship, but it is never too late to have this conversation for the first time.

Communication outside the Bedroom

The best way to communicate outside the bedroom is to have a conversation at a time when you are both unaroused, and your feelings won't be clouded by sexual frustration. If, after talking about this, you are both so horny that you go and jump on each other in the bedroom, that's fine, but begin this conversation in a different time and place so that it can be a serious dialogue about both of your needs.

Communication During Sex

During sex is an important time to check in with your partner to see how she is feeling, what she is liking, and what she wants more of. This is also a time where you can tell her what you like and what you want more of. While you are having sex, it is easiest to communicate using dirty talk so that you don't ruin the mood by coming off too serious or too concerned. In order to properly communicate while also playing into the mood of the moment, you can do so in a sexy way, using sexy language. You should tell each other what you like by saying, "oh yes, I like that" or "I like when you touch me like that" This lets the person know to do more of the same because this is what will get you to orgasm. If your girl seems like she is really enjoying what you are doing, don't change it up, keep doing the same. With a woman, if you find that thing she likes- don't give it up! It may be hard for you both to find the spot she likes and the way she likes it, so if she is getting hot and bothered by the way you are touching her, keep it up. You can ask her to let you know when she likes the way you are touching her and let her know that this will help you to give her great orgasms.

Communication After Sex

Next time you have sensual pillow talk, ask them what their favorite part was. Ask her what she liked and what you did that was different than before. You can open up this dialogue by telling her how sexy you thought she was or how you liked it when she did a certain thing to your penis. After sex is a good time for this because it is fresh in your minds and you can revisit it together while you both still remember exactly what you did to each other.

Spice Up Your Locations

If you want to try something different but feel like you have been trying many new positions and need something a little different yet, switching up your location can be just the thing you need! Pulling your pants down in a new location can make for a very hot and scandalous encounter. Having sex in a new environment makes things feel new and different and is exciting for you and your body! Now I'm not saying you need to go full-on public sex here, that will make you scared and unable to perform and not to mention will probably get you arrested. Just a small change in the environment can put your senses on high alert and will make you feel more of everything including pleasure when all of your senses including your touch is heightened.

In the Shower

Shower sex is steamy (literally) and hot (literally) and can make for some very fun body on body action. Make sure the water is the perfect temperature and that you have a mat or something on the floor so you aren't slipping all over the place! Before you start any type of penetration in the water make sure you use lots of waterproof lube because the water in the shower won't be enough of a lubricant for the inside of a vagina and will actually make for some painful friction. Let's avoid that, lube is your friend!

Standing Doggy Style

Standing Doggy Style is a good place to start with shower sex because it will make sure that you don't get sprayed in the face with a hot stream of water while you are trying to focus on having a blissful orgasm. Pleasurable for both parties, Doggy Style in the shower is a new take on an old favorite.

The man stands with his back to the running water with the woman standing in front of him, facing away from him. The woman then bends forward and can put her hands on the edge of the tub or the wall of the shower for support. The man slides his penis into her from behind, grabbing onto her hips for a deeper thrust and then they are ready to go for it. This position has a good chance of the man being able to hit the woman's G-spot with his penis, so this position will be greatly enjoyed by the woman. The warmth and the wet environment of the shower are sure to make for an unforgettable sexual encounter.

Kneeling Shower Sex

If you both are in the mood for a position that doesn't need you to focus too much on difficult positioning and holding yourselves up in a slippery shower, you can try the kneeling position. Have yourselves kneel on the floor of the shower, one person behind the other? From here you can go in many different ways. You can use this position as foreplay as you both reach around to pleasure the other's genitals with your hands before you move to the bedroom together. You can also use this as foreplay before switching to another position for penetration in the shower. Or you can start penetration right away. For penetration, you will have to adjust each of your heights on your knees to line up your erection and her vagina to meet nicely for smooth penetration. This position is full of possibilities and is a very hot way to get you both in the mood for whatever is to come either in the shower or out of it.

In the Car

Car sex is an old favorite, hailing from the days when we lived with our parents and had to find other places to get dirty than the single bed surrounded by posters of popstars. We couldn't risk being found out! Why not go back to those days where you were nervous and doe-eyed for a close encounter in the back seat of your car? Or if you lust after each other so strongly that you cannot wait to get home, pull over and rip each other's clothes off to have a car session right then and there! Having sex in the car gets the windows all steamy and the temperature rising. This hot little car has you all over each other, grinding on those old car seat cushions to the tune of the radio.

The Side Saddle

Sometimes, the positions that seem to be basic when you are at home and in bed may be that much more exciting when you are in a new environment, especially in a confined space. The Side Saddle is one of these positions.

166

The man sits in the back seat facing forward, the way you would normally sit in a driving car. The woman then sits on his lap across the back seat, facing the side window with her legs stretched across the back seats. The man now puts his penis inside the woman's vagina from here and can either thrust his hips up and down into her, or lift her up and down on his penis. This makes for a great use of the confined space of the back seat, giving both people enough room but is still confined enough to feel sexy and close. This position can be done discreetly and that makes it even sexier. Try imagining that you are in the back of a cab on your way home from the bar with a hot person you met that night. You are making out and are both so horny, itching to get into each other's pants and you simply can't wait any longer. The girl opens the buttons of your pants, lifts up her dress, slides onto your lap and you begin to have sex right then and there without the cab driver being any the wiser. You have to be as quiet as possible, stifling the moans of pleasure because you don't want him to find out what is going on in the back seat.

The Lap Dance

The Lap Dance is a more classic position but is just as hot as any other. This position doesn't need much setting up because at this point you would probably already be in the midst of a steamy car make out in this exact position. When you want to quickly transition from an innocent front seat make out to a full-blown hump session, this one is the quickest way to get down and dirty.

This position is done with the woman on top of the man as if she is giving him a lap dance, which is where it got its name. She is on his lap facing him with her legs on either side of his hips. You can even do this position with most of your clothes still on, to bring that element of urgency to your session and turn you on even more. The woman can take the man's penis out of his pants just enough to get access to it, slide her panties to the side and lower herself down onto his erection. From here, they are ready to go! They should be careful that she doesn't hit her head on the roof when she starts to get so into the mood that she is thrusting herself up and down with vigor. For another element of turn-on and closeness, the man can even hold onto the woman's head to protect this from happening. With his free hand, he can slide his fingers up her shirt and stimulate her nipples, or he can grab onto her butt cheeks. This position doesn't necessarily require penetration, so it is good for any combination of genders and genitals, it is just as easy to take each other's pants off before getting into the position and begin fingering each other or giving a hand job. Creativity is your friend in car sex!

In Public

Public sex is risky and you have to be sure that nobody else is around that will be scarred and greatly offended, but if not, it can be very exciting. Knowing that you are being naughty and rebellious is sure to ignite a fear-driven horniness deep within. The thrill of being outdoors or in public anywhere can make you feel free and uninhibited. Sharing this moment with the other person is sure to make you both giddy with a little healthy dose of the scariest. Outdoor sex and public sex can be two very different things, although outdoor sex usually comes with the chance that someone might see you.

Swimming Sex

This leads me to the swimming sex. Both outdoor and public, this one can be risky but very exciting if you do it the right way. Try having sex in the water, whether in a pool, in a lake, in the ocean or the hot tub. Water sex can be the place to try those tricky positions you want to try but maybe aren't strong or flexible enough to do on land. In the water, you are both virtually weightless and the water lets your joints move into positions they wouldn't be able to with all of that gravity here on earth. Because you are both so light, you can hold each other up or move each other around in ways you aren't normally able to.

Tree Hugger

The man is standing in water deep enough to cover his waist, preferably somewhere around the depth of his ribs or chest. The woman stands in front of him, facing him and then climbs into his arms, wrapping her legs around his waist and her arms around his neck. He will hold her up by her butt cheeks. Then, he can put his erection inside of her and do the thrusting with his arms by lifting her up and down on his penis.

This position is difficult to do on land, but in the water, you will be able to do it with ease. Being submerged so that you have just enough privacy will make you feel exposed enough to get turned on, but not too exposed so that you cannot concentrate on your pleasure. Your genitals will be safely hidden under the water and nobody will be able to see them unless you are in a crystal-clear sea (in which case you'll be like a fish in a fishbowl)! Her boobs can be hidden by a bikini, unless this is a nude beach or you are skinny dipping at night and then she could have her boobs pressed against your chest while you hold her. Talk about romance. Relax into the flotation that the water provides for your bodies and feel the pleasure that the other person is providing for you. Look at each other in the eyes or have a steamy make-out session while nobody knows what is really going on under the surface. For an added turn-on factor, you will have to be quiet and stifle your moans when you are close to orgasming so that nobody catches onto what is happening. Trying to keep quiet in intense pleasure only makes you more and more horny.

The Tree Hugger position is a great one for so many reasons. You are face to face so it is very intimate, supporting the weight of the woman's body isn't solely up to the man so he can let go of her cheeks every once in a while, and use his hands to explore her body.

Sex with Props

Sex Toys

Sex with toys can bring a new element of mystery and novelty to your sex life. It comes with new sensations and added pleasures that you may not have experienced before. Knowing where to start with toys in a world with countless varieties of uses, shapes, and sizes can be overwhelming at first, but here you will get an overview of where you can start and what positions you can use them in!

Vibrator

A vibrator can make a woman orgasm very intensely and in quite a short amount of time if her partner knows how to use it for her. When figuring out what your woman likes and how she likes to use her vibrator, make her the center of attention.

The Queen

Begin with her lying down on her back on the bed, relaxed and ready to receive your gifts of pleasure. Place yourself close to her genitals in a position that is comfortable and leaves your hands and arms free to move. You can try sitting cross-legged beside her or lying perpendicular to her, halfway down her body with the vibrator in your hand and the other hand free to roam. Start off very slow and gentle and find her clitoris with your fingers. Turn the vibrator on a low buzz, slowly bring it between her legs and place it so that it lightly touches her clitoris. From your position here beside her, you can turn your head to watch her facial expressions change as you try varying amounts of pressure and speed settings of the vibrator. Ask her if she likes it and use plenty of dirty talk. You can supplement this as well with your tongue every once in a while, and maybe even slip a finger inside her vagina and find her G-spot if she is comfortable. Listen to her desires and you will help her reach intense levels of pleasure. During all of this, you keep the vibrator on her clitoris. Adjust the speed if you can, increasing it as she gets wetter and wetter. After this, she will be feeling very horny and her vagina will be so wet that you will not need any lube for your next position. This position can be a starter in your session, or you can do it at the end to give her a happy ending.

Strap-On

A strap-on is another toy that can be used in a variety of ways to enhance your pleasure and your sex life. It is more common than you may imagine that in heterosexual sex, the woman will wear a strap-on and pleasure her male partner anally with it. This is called Pegging. While it is not for everyone, many men find pleasure from this because of the sensitivity of their prostate and many women find pleasure from this because they can see their man reaching higher levels of pleasure than ever before. This may be something you want to try.

Another situation where this toy would be a great inclusion would be in a lesbian relationship or two-vagina sex of any sort for that matter. One partner can wear the strap-on to penetrate the other partner either anally or vaginally.

Strap-On Doggy Style Anal Sex

Quite a mouthful to say, this position is a combination of a few other positions we have seen thus far. This position brings them all together to create a mecca of pleasure. Doggy style can be done with a strap-on to penetrate someone vaginally as we have seen already, but here we are going to look at Doggy Style Anal Sex.

When both people are fully turned on and horny for each other, the woman puts on the strap-on. Being sure to get the entire dildo and the anus covered with ample lube, she kneels behind her partner who is on all fours on the bed in front of her. After a little bit of play with her tongue or her fingers, she can slowly insert the dildo into her partner's anus and begin thrusting gently when it is relaxed and ready for it. While being penetrated with the strap-on, the person can touch their clitoris or rub their penis at the same time for even more stimulation and possibly even a double orgasm. The person wearing the strap-on can lean forward and put their body over their partner's body for more closeness and control.

Vibrating Ring

A Vibrating Cock Ring can be an amazing tool to take both male and female sex up a notch. The vibrating ring goes over the man's penis and down to the bottom of his shaft. This heightens his pleasure and he can use it during masturbation, but can also heighten the woman's pleasure when it is used during penetration. Sharing this with someone else during vaginal or anal sex can help you both have better orgasms. The other benefit of this ring is that it does not just enhance female pleasure from the vibrations it causes on the man's penis while it is inside of her, but also from the vibration it can give to the woman's clitoris when used in certain positions. The position we will examine is one that will benefit the female's clitoris.

During foreplay, as he is getting horny and his penis is getting hard, place the ring over the tip and slide it down to the base of his shaft, where it meets the testicles. The ring has a third function as it also keeps his penis harder for longer because it keeps the blood in his penis for longer. Turn on the vibration of the ring and he will have to try hard not to ejaculate yet as this will feel great on his penis.

Beyond the Bedroom

There are many ways to spice up your sex life, and as you learned there is a lot beyond the bedroom that can be done to enhance it as well.

Do Fun Things Together

Doing fun things together allows you to increase your dopamine levels together as well. When you have fun together, it increases your closeness with one another and can enhance the joy you experience with each other. It adds a unique sense of intimacy to your relationship that cannot be added by sexual experiences.

Ideally, you want to have fun together in a way that gets your blood pumping and your adrenaline rushing. Going to an amusement park, ice skating, visiting an upbeat concert, or otherwise doing something fun and exciting can increase the happiness of your experience with one another. Having fun this way can add an energy to your relationship that will carry into the bedroom and make sex even more enjoyable.

Kiss More Often

Many couples, especially those who have been together a while tend to kiss less often. Kissing is a highly romantic and passionate act and should be done regularly. Think about it, at the beginning of the relationship you likely kissed your partner a lot more frequently than you do now that you are more comfortable together. You want to start doing it more often.

When you are kissing more regularly, don't just increase the volume but also increase the passion in each kiss. There is no need to peck and go. Give the kiss a few moments and truly experience your partner with each kiss. You can include your hands and body as well, or even kiss in other intimate areas such as on the cheek, forehead or hand.

Recall What It Was Like to Meet

When you first met you likely spent a lot more time getting to know one another and a lot less time watching TV or doing other things to pass the time. You can spend some time asking each other questions about life, or even just reminisce on the days when you met each other. Getting to know each other all over again is a great way to rekindle the flame in a relationship.

The reality is that we don't all stay the same in life. Throughout your relationship, you and your partner will change several times over. Their preferences for certain things may change, and these are all great things to learn about each other all over again as you rekindle your love by communicating and asking questions.

Describe Your Sexual Fantasies

Many times, sex is just about the act and couples don't really speak a lot about sex outside of the bedroom. A great way to spark up a flame and add passion to your sex life is to talk about each other's fantasies and interests. This gives you an opportunity to get to know each other's sexual preferences more intimately which means that you can gain maximum enjoyment out of sex. It allows you to have a better idea of what your partner likes and what they don't like, and how you can make sexual experiences more enjoyable for them.

Keep the Mystery Alive

In relationships, it can be easy to get to know each other so intimately that there appears to be no mystery left in the relationship anymore. This can be counterproductive to the process of bringing romance back into your relationship. A lot of romance builds around mystery and the desire to know each other more intimately than you presently do. There are many ways that you can add mystery back into your relationship, even if you already know almost everything about each other. Using sentences that add mystery, clothes that spark intrigue and even simple texts that make the other partner wonder what you have planned for the evening can help add mystery back into the relationship.

When the mystery is present, the other person wonders about you. They start thinking about you and may even become obsessed with wanting to know what you have planned because they are curious. Curiosity is the key to creating mystery and getting your partner wondering about you and what you have to offer them that is unique from before.

Express Gratitude

A great way to help your partner feel cared for and show them how much they mean to you is to express your gratitude. Expressing gratitude takes very little time but can have a significant impact on the quality of your relationship. When people feel cared for and loved, they want to show more care and love to the one they feel for as well. This can increase the quality of your relationship, making you both feel more appreciated.

In relationships, the little things often get overlooked. People forget that the little things count and so they don't take the time to show appreciation and gratitude for them genuinely. Something as simple as "I really appreciate that you always support me in my decisions" or "I really appreciate that you make me breakfast each morning" can go a long way. Even though repeat activities can lead to things being expected, it is always good to show that you don't necessarily expect things to be done for you or in a certain way. Always show that you care about what your partner does in life and for you, as this will increase the quality of your time together and make you both feel more loved overall. When you feel more loved, the sparks will naturally fly in your relationship.

Don't Hold Grudges

Holding grudges can destroy relationships really quickly. When people hold grudges, they fail to let go of things that are no longer relevant, and it can lead to destruction in the relationship. You may feel that if you let go, it shows your partner that their mistake was acceptable, and for you, it may seem like you are allowing them to do it again. In reality, when you let it go, you are giving them permission to be human and make mistakes. It allows them the opportunity to see what they've done and make a change, knowing that you will appreciate the change wholeheartedly. It never pays to hold a grudge in your relationship.

Care About Self Care

How you care about yourself and how your partner cares about themselves is important when it comes to having a healthy relationship. A healthy relationship almost always leads to a healthy sex life, since your sex life is so closely linked to the health of your relationship. It is important that you both emphasize on self-care and take the time to truly nurture your own needs before nurturing your partner's. Yes, before. You cannot pour out of an empty cup, and keeping your cup empty is not a favor to your partner. Instead, it is a drawback that will lead to your relationship falling apart.

Taking care of your own self can come in many ways. You should look towards developing a healthy relationship with yourself if you want to really get serious about self-care. Take yourself on dates, have alone time, and get to know yourself more. The added benefit of getting to know yourself more is that you learn things about yourself that you may not have known before. You can share these things with your spouse, thus expanding your realm of conversation topics and letting you continue to get to know each other, even long after the relationship has worn out its honeymoon phase.

There are many ways that you can spark romance back into your relationship outside of the bedroom. By having these types of activities present in your day-to-day life, you increase the amount of romance and intimacy that lies between you and your partner and it causes for you both to become more eager about your sex life. A relationship that is rich outside of the bedroom is one that will be exciting inside of the bedroom.

When you are looking to cause sparks outside of the bedroom, you want to take your time and really get to know one another. Forget everything you've learned up until now and take the time to learn again. In many cases what you know now can be relevant but may no longer be the whole truth. People regularly change, and this can lead to there being a disconnection between what you are thinking and what your partner is wanting. By communicating, you can alleviate this disconnection and create a renewed sense of appreciation and romance between yourself and your partner.

Overall, the best thing you can do for your sex life is to nurture all areas of your relationship. The more successful your relationship is elsewhere, the more exciting your sex life will be. It creates a sense of deep knowing and trust that cannot be faked between two people. When this trust and love is present, the sex you experience will be unlike anything you have ever had before. Even relationships that have been alive for a long time can benefit from this type of rekindling.

Conclusion

Keeping things interesting in the bedroom is all about expanding from the norm. Everybody's regular sex involves something different, and it is up to you as a couple to determine what is normal and what is outside of that. For some, their normal maybe a Saturday night missionary until orgasm and then a cuddle for five minutes before watching television together for the rest of the night. For others, it may include sex nine times per week with a different role-play each night. For each of these couples, swapping routines with each other may even be enough to spice up their sex lives. Have a conversation with your partner and determine what your normal sex life looks like and what stepping out of that would entail.

Going forward, ensure that you are paying close attention to the sexual intelligence piece of the equation and ensure that you are remaining true to this first and foremost.

We must approach sex with a willingness to learn and grow for our entire lives, as none of us really reach a point where there is nothing more for us to learn on the topic. With new information, research, kinks, sexual groups and the like being thought of and put into practice each year, we can never stop discovering. This is not to say that we as sex masters much try everything we learn about and discover, but that we must be open to learning about it in order to find the things that we deeply desire.

It may feel uncomfortable or nerve-wracking at first, but the lasting results these conversations will produce are worth it.

CPSIA information can be obtained
at www.ICGtesting.com
Printed in the USA
BVHW092324220221
600780BV00007B/528